OVERLAPPING WORLDS

OVERLAPPING WORLDS

EXPLORING HOW NATURE SUPPORTS THE MENTAL HEALTH OF ELITE ATHLETES

OLIVIA GRACE BARNES

Kamilla — thank you so much for your support!!!

Olivia Grace

NEW DEGREE PRESS

OVERLAPPING WORLDS

Exploring How Nature Supports the Mental Health of Elite Athletes

ISBN   978-1-63730-818-9   *Paperback*

           978-1-63730-880-6   *Kindle Ebook*

           978-1-63730-970-4   *Ebook*

CONTENTS

———

INTRODUCTION

———

Imagine a beach. Imagine an empty horizon and beautiful waves that crash upon the shore. Imagine the calls of seagulls and the quiet solitude of the ocean breeze.

Now add cargo ships to that horizon. Add silt to the waves and replace their blue color with a murky brown. And instead of the quiet solitude of an ocean breeze, add the inescapable noises of cars, traffic, restaurants, and people. Welcome to Galveston Beach.

Unlike the beaches east of the Mississippi River, Galveston Beach is not blessed with white sands and clear water, but regardless of how obstructed and trashed this piece of nature is, without fail, I have always found peace in its rocking waves. The sounds of seawater rushing to meet my feet and the songs of the open ocean have always filled me with a quiet calmness, almost like the waves themselves as they ripple with the tranquility of the ocean wind.

And on a typical day at Galveston Beach, as I lay within the waves, I saw my first dolphin.

The moment was pure and sincere. I was not watching that dolphin from a film, a zoo, or an aquarium, nor from a whale-watching boat. It was simply me and the dolphin in the murky waters, both at peace in the soothing waves. It was almost as if, for the briefest of moments, the untouched and flawless world of nature showed me its beauty and grace.

I had spotted its dorsal fin first, sleek and gray as it crested the waves, and although I had originally thought a shark was swimming in the waters in front of me, I soon realized I was seeing my first wild dolphin. The fear that had initially rushed through my veins was quickly replaced by a feeling of wonder as it swam only a couple of feet away from my fingertips.

Although my life and the life of that cloudy charcoal-gray dolphin overlapped only for a second, that moment was one of the most defining moments in my life. In that brief instant, it was as if I became part of something bigger and more beautiful than I could ever imagine. But not only was I part of this bigger something, but I also belonged there as well. That dolphin awed me to the point of reverence, and as its dorsal fin slipped below the surface and vanished below the waves, I began to cry.

Mental illness is a global pandemic.

Unlike the world-flipping COVID-19, this pandemic is not frequently talked about, there are few international efforts to end its presence, and those who suffer from it suffer in silence. But very similar to the coronavirus, mental health issues affect individuals in almost every country and can make people extremely vulnerable to sickness and death.

And although a wide range exists in the severity of mental illness, *everybody* is susceptible, including athletes. A heart-breaking statistic acknowledges that around 80 percent of Olympic athletes struggle with some kind of post-Olympic depression, and on this stage, I have begun to explore how to end the silence around mental illness in athletic communities and support those who need help.

As I look back on that day when I saw my first wild dolphin, I know now that my tears originated from a place of true and genuine awe: the combination of fear and happiness. It was the kind of awe inspired by the power and beauty only the natural world contains.

Over the course of my lifetime, I have had many experiences in nature, and I observed a common factor. Almost every time I spend time in nature, I return with an improved mental state. Whether it is simply the prolonged presence of peace or something more profound, nature has proven itself to have the power to affect the mind positively.

But why are these mental powers of nature important? And how do they play a role in ending the pandemic of athletes with mental illnesses?

Well, if athletes need help mentally, and nature can positively affect the mind, what if nature could be a remedy? What if it could help support athletes' mental health and change their lives for the better? I believe that nature itself has the potential to lower the presence of mental illness drastically in athletic communities, but I also know that until the social stigmas around mental health fade, athletes will continue to struggle in silence.

I write this book through the lens of nature as a psychological power and mental illness as a global pandemic, as I explore the topics of athletics, mental health, and the environment. And while these three topics might seem disjointed, their intersection sheds light on the beauty and strength of these three overlapping worlds. Being a competitive swimmer since the age of six, an environmental enthusiast from the time I was born, and a victim of mental health issues myself, I am compelled to write this book for fellow competitive and elite athletes because I believe that three things need to change:

1. Awareness and open conversation around mental health must become normal.
2. Spending habitual and quality time in nature needs to become a priority.
3. Support of athletes, both mentally and physically, in athletic communities must become a *necessity*.

Through interviews, stories, and research from experts, I hoped to uncover a world where these changes can become common practice. My desire to address these issues has led me from a simple interest to a calling to speak up and speak out. With my unique platform, along with the support and guidance of others, I hope this book will shape and inspire change in our world.

Throughout *Overlapping Worlds*, I will uncover how nature affects the mental health of athletes and explore how it can help strengthen, maintain, and support the health of elite competitors. And while I geared this book toward my fellow competitive athlete, I hope *any* reader can find use and inspiration from the compiled stories, interviews, and research within.

PART I

BEHIND THE MIND

CHAPTER 1

BEHIND THE MINDS
OF ATHLETES

A single race changed the entire trajectory of my life. It was a relay, one of the most memorable of all time, and I didn't even know it happened until almost six years after the fact.

Five colors, five rings, countless flags, one world, united.

This was the Beijing Olympic Games.

With blinding lights illuminating the water and spectators packing the stands full, the eight teams marched onto the pool deck for the finals of the men's 4x100 meter freestyle relay. A hush filled the natatorium as the swimmers took their mark upon the block. The athletes cocked every muscle in anticipation of the horn and directed every sense toward the pool.

And in a sudden beep, the race had begun.

From the very beginning, it was a battle for gold between the American and French athletes. The lead seesawed from one team to the other as the first, then second, and then third athlete raced their leg of the event. But even though the entire race was a captivating experience, the final 100 meters truly sent shivers down my spine as I watched that fight for victory.

As the final legs of the relay—Lezak for Team USA and Bernard for Team France—entered the water, the French relay had a defined lead on America, and at the 50 wall, Lezak was behind by almost a full body length. It looked as if the gold medal for the French team was inevitable.

But as they crossed the halfway point of the second 50, something remarkable happened. It wasn't obvious at first, but as the distance between the two swimmers began to shrink, it became clear that Lezak had not given up on gold. Pouring on power and speed, Lezak rapidly gained on Bernard until they were dead even. And with only a few feet from the wall, Jason Lezak took his last stroke, out-touching Alain Bernard and the French team by only 0.08 seconds and setting a new world record! From the screams of Michael Phelps, Garret Weber-Gale, and Cullen Jones (the other members of Team USA's relay) to the cheers of the crowd and to the shouts of the announcers as well, the excitement from that victory was palpable.

This race is one of the few races that excites me without fail. Although I have watched it countless times and already know the outcome, it remains forever engaging. And every single time I watch it, I can feel the emotion radiating from my computer or phone screen.

The men's 4x100 meter relay at the 2008 Olympics is an unforgettable race for many reasons. First, all eight relays in that event broke the 3:13 barrier, making the entire final a historically fast heat. Second, Phelps, who led off the relay for Team USA, set an American record of 47.51 seconds but still only touched the wall almost half of a second behind than the Australian athlete Eamon Sullivan, who had set a *world record* on his leg of the race. Third, Alain Bernard, the anchor of the French relay, was the former world record holder in the 100m freestyle but still was unable to keep his lead from Lezak. Also, Jason Lezak swam a once-in-a-lifetime race with the fastest 100m freestyle split to this day with a time of 46.06 as he anchored that relay. And finally, this race marked one of the eight races that Michael Phelps won at that Olympics, setting a record in the process of the most gold medals won in a single Olympic Game.

I say that this race changed my life forever because as I grew up watching races like it, I developed not only a love for competition but an eagerness to push myself, both mentally and physically, to my limits. This men's 4x100m freestyle relay will go down in history as one of the greatest races *ever*, and as I continue to grow deeper in my athletic career, I can't help but wonder what was going through the minds of those athletes, French and American alike, as they made history.

Being a swimmer myself, I can imagine what was going through Bernard's head as he tried to fight off Lezak in the last 25, or even 15 meters of their 100m freestyle. I can imagine how fatigued his muscles were and how much pain he would have been in. I can imagine how determined he was to win, but how upsetting it was to see Lezak close such a big gap so quickly. I can even imagine the mental pain he might have gone through during those last few meters as he did everything in his power to maintain his lead.

But even though I am a very accomplished swimmer, I have yet to compete on a stage as big as the Olympics and have no idea what the pressure and intensity might be like to be a world-class athlete like Jason Lezak or Alain Bernard. I know that I am not alone in being curious about what it is like to compete on a major stage. Whether through the post-race interviews or the commentary of announcers, clearly the prowess and capabilities of these athletes similarly fascinates the world, as does the behind-the-scenes—or better put, behind-the-mind—aspects of elite competitors.

My biggest questions are:

- What goes through the athlete's mind before, during, and after a monumental and exciting match or race like that 4x100 relay?
- How does it compare with other performances, specifically extremely *disappointing* performances?
- And how do athletes respond to and handle the pressure of being on a highly competitive stage, whether a national or international competition?

Through the stories and interviews of several high-level athletes, I have begun to learn more about and uncover what goes on within the mind of an athlete. And if you have ever wanted to meet or converse with an Olympic gold medalist and learn their secrets, have ever dreamed about standing in the presence of a true athletic prodigy, or have ever wondered what it would be like to watch the journey of an up-and-coming star, then you are in the right place. The athletes I will cover during these next three chapters are Michael Marsh, two-time Olympian (two gold and one silver); Jack Armstrong, one-time Junior Worlds Attendee; and Elizabeth Beisel, three-time Olympian (one silver and one bronze). Through each of their unique experiences and insights, I will give you a deeper understanding of what goes on inside the minds of elite athletes.

CHAPTER 2

MICHAEL MARSH

———

*"Always make a total effort, even
when the odds are against you."*

—ARNOLD PALMER

MICHAEL MARSH

1993, Stuttgart, Germany.

It was the men's final of the 1993 Track and Field World
Championships.

Supporters from all around the world packed the stadium,
each cheering for his or her respective country and hopeful
for a victory. Flags waved across the stands, representing
the USA, Spain, Zimbabwe, Cuba, and the other 183 nations
present. Cameras flashed like luminescent fireflies, burst-
ing through the audience with blinding white lights. Of this
nine-day international competition, today was day number
seven, and the race of the evening was the men's 200m final.

This event had started out with close to ninety athletes, but through four rounds of intensely competitive racing (preliminaries, quarterfinals, semifinals, and finals), only the fastest eight remained. The stadium erupted in cries and cheers as these eight men stepped onto the track, each putting their mind in the zone, preparing for the moment when they would have to race. Six countries represented themselves in this event final: Australia in lanes 1 and 3, Ghana in lane 2, the USA in 4 and 7, Namibia in 5, Great Britain in 6, and France in 8. The cameras zoomed in on the athletes as the commentators announced each name to the world. But while those in the stands watched each athlete in awe, one man in particular held the audience's and announcer's attention.

With the typical American red, white, and blue, his track uniform stood out against his competitors. The swirling design gave way to the three large letters that rested on the center of the shirt. His two bibs hung on his front and back, reading the numbers 1321 as he paced back and forth in his lane, staring down the track as it curved toward the finish line. And after he shook the hands of several of his competitors, he blocked out the noise and distractions of the audience and cameras around him and focused only on himself and the race that lay ahead.

The runner drawing everyone's attention was Michael Marsh.

From the eyes of the world watching, Michael had this race in his pocket. Since he was both the current American record holder in the 200m and the defending Olympic champion in the same race, a victory might appear promised, but to Michael himself, the road to the finish line was a lot more complicated. Throughout the entire competition, Michael had been struggling with severe pain on the outside of his left leg. Competing one event four times through is challenging enough for *any* athlete, and it was especially grueling for Marsh. Pushing himself through the three previous races in the prelims, quarterfinals, and semifinals, Michael was grateful to have simply *made* it to the final eight athletes. But as the finals approached, the pain in his leg did not subside.

But long before the race began, these athletes were in warm-up. The supporters were not cheering for the men's 200m, the lights were not flashing, nor had the cameras begun to zoom in on the eight athletes, watching their every move and analyzing the suspected victor. Each of those competitors was warming up for their race, both mentally and physically preparing for speed.

While Michael begged his body to hold together, pleading for twenty seconds of race time and promising rest and recovery to his pained leg as soon as the race was over, his body did not comply. As Michael soon found out, his body had the power to veto any request of the mind, which is just what his body did. Although this World Championship race was extremely important, the negative effects that would result from sacrificing his health for the gold and glory could not outweigh the positive effects of obtaining victory. His body understood that fact, and as warm-ups wore on, his mind began to realize it as well.

Finally, it was time for the race. The eight athletes stepped onto the track amid deafening cheers and screams from the crowd. People from all around the world packed the stadium full to the brim as the athletes lined up in their lanes for the final of the men's 200m. After pacing back and forth while the commentators announced each competitor, the world watched as the men placed their feet on the blocks and waited for the gun to blow. Michael was not afraid of the race before him but determined to do his best with what he had to give.

"Set," the official spoke through the mic. Then...*Crack!*

The gun went off, and so did the eight. Sacrificing his momentum for the health of his leg, Michael intentionally backed off the first several strides, giving several men around him an uncatchable lead. Ten seconds in, he rounded the curve, turning into the final stretch of the race. And although he had lost any hope of gaining a lead, he still did his best, pulling ahead of the fourth-place runner and crossing the finish line in fourth. His teammate, Carl Lewis, had finished third.

The stadium erupted in cheers, celebrating the outstanding victory from Namibian athlete Frank Fredricks. And as the other seven athletes walked out of their race, striding across the lanes of the track and basking in the glory and praise of competing on such an impressive stage, Michael Marsh's pain became visible. He did not wince as he walked off the track and his face held no emotion with each step, but the limp in his gait gave it away.

After the race, Marsh flew to Denver, Colorado, a location known for its high quality and quantity of orthopedic doctors because of the constant knee-related injuries from skiers in the nearby mountains. Michael's doctor ordered an MRI but reported that everything looked normal. Michael could barely walk at that point because the pain was so severe, so he knew something was wrong with his knee. After extensive communication with the doctor, he asked for exploratory surgery.

As the surgeon opened his knee and searched for the source of the pain, he uncovered a bone spur that had been hidden from view during the MRI behind another bone. Using precision tools and meticulous care, the doctor removed the bone spur and finished the surgery successfully.

Michael recovered quickly, and in about six weeks, he was back on his feet, training once more. The next year, he competed again, setting a couple of world records with his teammates in the process.

I have known Michael Marsh, or Mr. Mike Marsh as my siblings and I called him, for as long as I can remember. He and his family lived two blocks away from mine, and in our urban neighborhood that consisted primarily of elderly inhabitants, his three sons and my siblings and I became close childhood friends. From attending each other's birthday parties to constantly hanging out in parks or going on bike rides together, the Marsh and Barnes kids could often be seen in close proximity. Our ages overlapped almost perfectly, and relays and competitions were a common practice whenever we hung out.

As we grew up, even though my siblings had about a year and a half lead on each respective Marsh boy, it became increasingly hard to beat them in backyard running races. What had once been an easy win for me and my siblings soon became countless humiliating losses until we gave into the facts and stopped challenging the Marshes to short sprints.

My siblings and I were all competitive swimmers growing up. We knew we would dominate in the water, but on land, the Marsh boys would *always* have the victory.

Although my siblings and I no longer had the luxury of winning running races against the Marshes, we remained good friends. In fact, for the 2008 Beijing Olympics, the Marsh family invited us to their house to watch the Games. Although it was the second Olympics since I was born, it was the first Olympics I could watch. While my recollection of the Games is patchy, I remember clearly a comment my mom made several years later about those Olympic Games.

I was probably six or seven when my mom told me that Mr. Mike Marsh was an Olympian. She had been talking about the Beijing Olympics and how exciting it was when she casually mentioned that Mr. Mike Marsh had once competed at the Olympics in track and field for Team USA.

And I could not believe it.

For starters, I had never seen Mr. Mike Marsh run in my entire life, so picturing him competing with the fastest in the world was challenging. I had also only ever seen him as Mr. Mike Marsh— my neighbor, my friend, a friendly and sociable guy whom I considered uncle-like. But an Olympian? I simply couldn't wrap my head around it.

Seeing my disbelief, my mom sat me down then and there, and, pulling out her computer, we watched one of Mike Marsh's Olympic relays. And there he was. A lot younger than I had known him, for sure, but it was still him. His speed was unbelievable and undeniable, and in that instant, I finally understood why his kids so effortlessly beat my siblings and me in running races: they had been blessed by their father's world-class running gene.

Included among Michael's numerous talents is his ability to tell stories. Through countless stories about his experience in the world of competitive track and field, he gave me my first glimpse into what goes on behind the mind of elite athletes. And in April 2021, I had the privilege of interviewing Michael Marsh for this book.

Viewing Michael's 200m race in the 1993 Worlds through his eyes was a fascinating experience. While his pre-race calculation, his intentionality within the race, and his post-race process shed light on what went through his mind, I was still curious about whether his response to that race was a one-time thing or whether it was his consistent reaction to pressure, pain, and a world-class stage. Michael's 200m race in Stuttgart, Germany, was his most exciting, and so I was curious about what he considered his most *disappointing* race.

This race was the men's finals of the 100m at the American Olympic Trials, and although the Olympic trials is an extremely exciting meet and the singular deciding event of who will become members of the Olympics' Team USA, conditions were not ideal for competition. The outdoor stadium opened up to the scorching 107-degree heat, and the track burned so hot that the athletes had to pour water on the ground to keep their hands from burning as they crouched at the start.

On top of that, three false starts had occurred, including one where all the athletes had run a full 40m before the officials stopped the race. Everyone was exhausted.

As Michael and I talked about this race, he shared with me what was going through his mind after that third false start. I found his thought process fascinating.

> *The good thing though is once you get to that level of competition, you understand that I'm exhausted, but everyone else had to go through the same thing, so I'm at no disadvantage. We're all exhausted.*

While it might have been tempting to become discouraged by the heat and multiple false starts, Michael addressed the situation with an extremely clear and level head. He understood that while his performance might have been affected by temperature or fatigue, he was no worse off than anyone else. The mark of an elite competitive athlete is remaining calm in the face of adversity, which is just what Michael did.

But while Michael kept his cool and held his emotions in check during the scorching heat and the numerous false starts, it was a different story once the race started.

> *In track and field, anytime you react to a competitor, that's a mistake because track and field is very focused. You get from point A to point B as fast as possible. You*

have a plan, and anybody else's plan has no bearing upon yours. I was an incredibly strong finisher, and my coach always told me not to worry about my position early in the race. He told me over and over again, they hand out medals at the end, so it doesn't matter what your position is. But parts of your brain are very primitive, and they can overpower you under pressure.

Right in the middle of the race, I made a critical mistake, which I've been taught over and over and over again not to do. One of my competitors pulled ahead, and for only about four or five strides, I pressed and tried to catch him, or at least keep him from moving too far ahead of me. And I was not ever, ever supposed to do that.

But then I relaxed, and at the end, like I usually do, I started to move on the field like a horse. And what we call it is I ran out of track. I took fourth place by 0.01 seconds. And the fastest three people go to the Olympic team.

Missing out on the Olympic team is devastating. Missing it by only a hundredth of a second, even more so. And for a simple mistake?

That's my most disappointing because it was completely, completely 100 percent my fault. I should have been on that team, and I wasn't. It's just that simple. Do it in practice, do it in competition. But the silver lining is I learned the lesson. I had another chance to make the team in the 200 that year, and I did not make that mistake again. I made the team and ended up winning the gold medal.

What's truly interesting about both Michael's most exciting and his most disappointing race is *why* he categorizes them as he does. Ironically, Michael placed fourth in both races, but his responses are quite contrasting.

As Michael looked back on that race twenty-eight years after it happened, he told me that the finals of the men's 200m at the World Championships was the most exciting race he had ever run. He didn't forget the intense pain and discomfort he had experienced at and after that World Championship in 1993. Nor did he ignore the disappointment of being unable to add to his title of being the American record holder and defending Olympic champion. And by no means did his memory of his six-week-long post-race recovery fade from his mind.

Michael remembered every negative part of that race, and remembered it in detail, but the pain didn't define that race for him but the *effort*. That 200m was the most exciting race because he did his best with what he was given. Maybe he couldn't defend his titles, and maybe he missed the podium, but he placed *fourth* with a bone spur! In Michael's mind, it was an outstanding victory. Few others would deem this as Michael Marsh's most exciting race, but Michael gave it his all, and to him, that was what mattered.

In that 200m at World Championships, Michael was injured and was not *physically* capable of competing well. Nevertheless, by putting himself into a productive and effective mindset, he pulled out an internal victory. Although in the world's eyes, that race might not have been Michael's best, Michael was aware of his own limitations. In that race, he pushed himself to the limit.

However, in his 100m at the Olympic trials in 1988, although Michael was physically capable, his *mind* got in the way of his ability, a couple of strides interfered with months and years of hard work, and he missed out on his opportunity to make the team in that event.

As we talked, it became clear that Michael was very intentional about regulating his response to pressure during his track and field career. Although he couldn't monitor his response to pressure in every event or at every competition, acknowledging the pressure, creating a thought process around that pressure, and *then* deciding how to react is one of the critical ways in which Michael remained emotionally strong and mentally prepared even when competing on national, international, and, eventually, Olympic stages. He said:

> *I think you have to have thinking mechanisms to help you calm yourself in those situations and to stay in control. But you need the adrenaline because to have incredibly high performances, you have to be right on the edge of out of control.*

Sometimes the body is not in prime condition to compete, and the mind is required for strength. On the flip side, sometimes the weakness of the *mind* affects the capabilities of the body. Finding the balance between control and out of control, as Michael put it, can be extremely challenging. Overall, Michael's stories emphasize that having both a strong body and a strong mind is *crucial* for competitive athletes.

While looking at those two races through the eyes of Michael Marsh himself, it's clear to me he didn't get the balance right *all* the time, but through his numerous national, World Championship, and Olympic victories that he stacked up through the years, he clearly found that balance eventually.

RECAP

CHAPTER OBJECTIVES:
Answering the questions from Behind the Minds of Athletes:

- What went through Michael Marsh's mind before, during, and after the men's 200-meter final at the 1993 World Championships?
  - Before the race, Michael focused on how he could run the race considering his limitations (bone spur).
  - During the race, Michael focused only on doing the best he could with what he was given.
  - After the race, Michael focused primarily on the recovery and rehabilitation of his leg.
  - This race was primarily a physical game: his mind was prepared, but his body was not.
- How did those responses compare with the men's 100-meter final at the 1992 Olympic Trials?
  - Similar to his most exciting race, Michael focused on how he could run the race considering his limitations (fatigue from the heat and three false starts).

- Contrasting his most exciting race, Michael focused on his competitors instead of his own run during the race.
- Contrasting his most exciting race again, Michael focused on learning from his mistakes and preparing his mind after his race had ended.
- This race was primarily a mental game: his mind was not as prepared as his body.
- And how did Michael respond to and handle the pressure of being on a highly competitive stage?
  - Michael understood that the mind played a critical role in his ability to perform well and, therefore, highly prioritized both his physical and mental strength.
  - Michael also responded to effort more than results. If his effort was high, it was a success. On the flip side, if his effort was low or wasted, it was the opposite.

KEY TAKEAWAYS:
- **Effort** has more weight than public victories or losses.
- **Mental** and **physical strength** are both necessary for high-quality performances.

CHAPTER 3

JACK ARMSTRONG

——

"It's not whether you get knocked
down; it's whether you get up."

—VINCE LOMBARDI

JACK ARMSTRONG
I think speed is like a butterfly.

Why? Well, because it is often very easy to forget about how much effort and time goes into creating both butterflies and speed. Also, they are both pretty cool to watch in action.

But other than that, speed and butterflies have nothing in common.

Jack Armstrong has been blessed with more speed than anyone I know. So in a sense, I guess Jack is also like a butterfly.

From the first time I met Jack, around five or six years ago, until now, his speed has been undeniably impressive. Because

I train with a club swim team in one of the most competitive swimming states in the country, I have had a lot of experience competing against extremely talented athletes. Even so, I have always known that Jack was by far the fastest swimmer I had ever seen. Growing up watching him swim both at practice and meets, I began to understand the skill, patience, and intentionality, on a very practical level, it takes to become an elite-level swimmer.

But while Jack's highly competitive swimming career has gained serious traction and attention over the years, he still gives credit to his mother, who first encouraged him to explore and stick to the sport. While water polo had originally been his favorite sport, his mother emphasized that if he wanted to be competitive at water polo, he would *have* to be a good swimmer as well.

Jack took his mother's advice to heart. And while he had originally only committed to one full year of competitive swimming, as he began to swim more and more, his interest in the sport spiked as well. After a couple of years, Jack stopped playing water polo entirely. By the time he was around fifteen, he had truly begun to take swimming seriously.

The sport of swimming has a wide range of event and stroke specialization, but while some struggle to identify where they should specialize, the paradox of choice did not affect Jack: from the beginning, he knew that he flourished best in sprinting. With a bit of a laugh, Jack told me as I interviewed him about his athletic career that when he first began swimming, his one goal in the pool was to beat the guy next to him.

"I didn't really want to practice; I just wanted to race."

But while, with age, Jack grew to accept practicing, racing still excited him most. Specializing in the shortest and fastest races of the sport, the 50 and 100 freestyle, Jack continually lit up the pool with his incredible speed. And although he was known to beat swimmers by full-body lengths in local meets, he also proved he could be incredibly fast on national and international stages.

In the summer of 2019, Junior Worlds was the biggest meet Jack Armstrong had ever attended. Not only was it his first international competition, but other athletes, coaches, and spectators also viewed it all over the world: an experience of a lifetime.

The 2019 Junior World Championships was held in Budapest, Hungary, and comprised the fastest fifteen-to-eighteen-year-old men and fourteen-to-seventeen-year-old women in the world. But while racing for Team USA was a critical point in Jack's swimming career, his journey in Budapest didn't start on the first day of that meet. While a lifetime of training had led him up to this point, one full year of fighting, in particular, had taken him from a statewide and junior national athlete to a junior *world* competitor.

This fight began in the late summer months of 2018 at the Phillips 66 Nationals, a highly competitive annual competition

JACK ARMSTRONG · 37

for the fastest swimmers in America. Seven weeks prior to this meet, Jack was in game mode. His times and splits in practice were on point. He was consistently handling sets. His feel for the water was superb, and he felt extremely ready and prepared for the meet ahead. And even though he did not swim *all* the sets his coach assigned or race in every single meet that summer, he knew he was ready. As the weeks crept by and Nationals grew closer and closer, Jack felt the pressure increase and his confidence rise as well. He was physically prepared, he was mentally charged, and he knew that Nationals would be an eventful meet.

But once the meet started, however, nothing went according to plan. From the moment he got there, he realized something was off. He couldn't grab the water, and everything he felt in the weeks preceding the race, all the readiness and hype, seemed to have vanished. Jack was fully tapered, shaved, and teched up, but still, his races were not going the way he had planned. Jack was trying his first attempt to make the Junior National Team and represent Team USA at the Junior World Championships, but although he had been confident in making the team seven weeks prior, his hopes were beginning to crumble before his eyes.

All the sets he skipped and the meets he missed the weeks prior hit him like a wave. And in his 100m freestyle, all the mental preparedness he thought he had seemed to fly out the window as he almost gave up in the last thirty-five meters of that race.

It only took half of the meet for Jack to realize it wouldn't turn out the way he wanted. Frustrated at his inability to hold on to the water and determined to end the meet that was snowballing into disaster, he looked for help. Begging his coach to find him a weight room then and there, Jack admitted he was mentally exhausted. Yet he was so motivated by his failure at Nationals that he was ready to start lifting, training, and getting better as soon as possible.

Although he didn't literally find a weight room and start lifting at Nationals, he did stand by his word. His disappointment fueled him, and he made sure that the next time he had the opportunity to attempt making the Junior National team, he would be both physically *and* mentally ready.

The next chance Jack had to swim at a national competition was in December 2018, only a couple of months after his disastrous Nationals. This time, it was Winter Junior Nationals, a biannual selective and extremely competitive competition for the fastest swimmers in the country under age eighteen.

Leading into the competition, Jack's first race was the 50 free. Speed was Jack's specialty, and in prelims, he put on a show. Entering the meet, Jack was *not* the number 1 seed, but after a spectacular performance in prelims, not only was Jack the only person to go faster than twenty seconds in the 50 free, but he had also beaten his biggest rival in the process; he claimed the first-place spot for finals. But while winning in prelims was fun, in finals was where it truly mattered—when the points got scored and the prizes got dealt. With excitement and anticipation, Jack prepared to swim in the finals that evening.

After prelims ended, there was a several-hours break before the races of the evening. And after prioritizing nutrition and recovery in the competition-free afternoon, Jack was both physically and mentally prepared for his 50 free that night. As he warmed up before his race, his feel for the water was still there, as was his speed. After clocking several fast times in a couple of warm-up sprints, Jack knew he was ready. Exiting the warm-up pool and drying off, he visited his coach for a short strategic conversation before heading to the ready rooms.

Soon it was time to race. As the announcer called the final of the men's 50-yard freestyle out from the ready room, the eight athletes walked onto the pool deck amid cheers from their supporters. People packed the natatorium. Teammates, coaches, and officials watched from the side, crowding together on the pool deck, while spectators, family members, and friends filled the stands.

For those watching the meet online, the camera focused in on each athlete as they were announced. Jack, being the fastest from prelims, was in lane four, and as his name was called, the cameraman trained in on Jack's face. He smiled and waved to the audience before pulling on his cap and shutting out anything that might distract him from victory. The tension in the air was palpable and thick as the eight swimmers prepared to race, and as Jack stood behind the blocks, he had his beast mode turned on.

When the whistle blew for the athletes to mount the blocks, the cries and cheers died down, and when the official called, *Take your mark...* the entire natatorium was hushed. But once the horn rang out, all chaos broke loose. As the eight men dove in and began their race, everyone was cheering for them. The shouts and cries grew louder as they flipped on the first wall and began heading back toward the finish. The entire group was neck and neck, making it almost impossible to predict who the victor might be, but when the eight of them slammed against the wall, the scoreboard told no lies. In first place, with a time of 19.81 seconds, was Jack Armstrong. Slapping the water with excitement, Jack stared at the board as the crowd cheered. Not only had he won prelims, but he had also pulled out a win in finals as well, earning a victory and gaining a Junior National gold.

The next day Jack swam the 100 fly. While his time in that race wasn't a bad time, Jack didn't even make finals in that event, a surprising result from the athlete who had *won* the 50 free the day before. But holding his mind by the reins, Jack didn't let that race faze him. Maintaining a mindset of confidence and courage, Jack continued the meet, eventually winning both prelims and finals in the 100 free the day after and earning his second gold of the meet.

After a stellar meet at the 2018 Winter Junior Nationals, Jack continued his training, keeping his momentum going and focusing on the goal he had set of making it to the Junior Team USA for the Junior World Championships. And several months after Junior Nationals, Jack had his second chance of making the Junior National team.

It was the Phillips 66 National Championship in Palo Alto, California, at Stanford University's Aquatic Center. But while the pressure was heavy during this meet, Jack responded to it, not letting it mess with his feel for the water like it had the year before. This time, he was truly prepared, both physically and mentally, for the races to come.

Astonishing both himself and his team, he dropped a significant amount of time in both his 50 and 100 freestyle, making not one but *two* Olympic Trials qualifying cuts in the process. But while Jack was delighted by those results, the pleasant surprises did not end there. After clocking 50.05 in his 100-meter freestyle, several coaches noticed Jack and invited him to be part of Team USA at the Junior Worlds Championship soon after.

Only a few weeks after the 2019 National Championship, Jack boarded a flight to Budapest, Hungary, for his first ever Junior Worlds. After getting free clothes and having his flight paid for, he truly felt a part of Team USA. It was an honor and a long-lived dream he was unbelievably grateful to have come true. He arrived a couple of days early to get used to the pool and environment, but in no time, the meet was in full swing.

Jack had been invited to be part of Team USA's men's 4x100m freestyle relay in prelims, which took place on the first day of the meet. Nervousness and excitement flooded through him and his relay mates as they prepped for their race. And after warming up and drying off, they waited to be called out and announced to the world.

Walking through the tunnel as the words "Team USA" flooded the natatorium, Jack and his teammates were met with light, music, and cheers as they walked onto the deck.

As Jack stared around Budapest's heavily crowded Danube Arena, he could feel the pressure filling him with energy and motivation. He could feel his national pride giving him a power beyond the stars and stripes that lined the flag on his cap. Two big screens showed live footage from cameras around the pool, highlighting its beauty and pristine water. The light was dim around the bleachers, but the pool glowed from the underwater lights, drawing the eye toward the yellow lane lines and the ten black stripes that lined the bottom.

Unlike most meets, where the maximum number of occupied lanes per heat capped off at eight lanes, all ten lanes were in use at Junior Worlds, filled by teams from Kenya, Jamaica, Brazil, Japan, Russia, the USA, Canada, Mexico, Pakistan, and Ukraine, respectively. The race was about to begin.

As the whistle blew, a long shrill blow that signaled the athletes to get on the blocks, the tension rose in anticipation. The ten men crouched, their eyes focused on the still glassy water beneath and their ears straining for the horn. And once it went off, they flew from the blocks, entering the water and racing to the surface with unbelievable speed.

The cheers from the stands and the din from the splashes of the swimmers added up to a roar within the natatorium, and after about twenty-three seconds, the fastest members of that wave hit the first 50 wall. The USA touched first, with Ukraine and Brazil following close behind. But the winner of that first 50m was not necessarily the winner of the whole 100m, for as the men neared the end of their second 50m, the order of leads rearranged—with Canada leading, followed by Russia and then the USA.

The leads changed back and forth between the five leading teams as the next leg of the relays entered the water and swam their portion of the race. When the second leg of the relays neared the wall, Brazil, the USA, and Russia remained within almost 0.2 seconds of one another. Now it was Jack's turn to race.

After watching his two teammates battle for the lead, he was determined to do the same and help Team USA to a prelim victory. As he stood on the blocks, his eyes followed the second leg as it passed the 15-meter mark, then the flags, then… as his teammate touched the wall, Jack was off.

Leaping from the blocks, he entered the water slightly behind Brazil, but by the time both athletes surfaced, Jack was in a distinguishable lead. Grabbing the water with power, Jack flew across the pool, and by 45m, he was a full body length in front of all the competition. Adrenaline coursed through his veins as he reached the wall and flipped, channeling his energy and power toward the other side of the pool. Trying to maintain speed, he raced toward the finish. But while he was breathing toward his left, the third leg of the Brazilian team began to creep up on his right. Instead of following a racing plan, Jack had been so full of excitement that he had messed up his pacing for that 100m, taking it out much faster than he should have.

Regardless, Jack pushed himself, determined to give the anchor of his relay an unbeatable lead. But while he did not manage to stay a full body length ahead of the competition, he did manage to hold off the Brazilian, touching the wall first and securing a lead for his teammate.

Exhausted from his race, Jack hung on the wall and lane rope, catching his breath for a few seconds before hoisting himself out of the water and cheering for the anchor of his relay. The USA relay team ended up winning prelims, getting the number one seed for finals. While Jack was not accepted into Team USA's relay in the finals, he did watch as his teammates won the gold and set a junior world record in the process.

Although Jack had only been initially invited to compete in the 4x100m freestyle prelim relay, on the last day of the meet, four days after his first race, he was invited to anchor the men's 4x100m medley relay as well. Taking the opportunity, Jack honored Team USA by competing in his second race for America, helping his team win the prelims and indirectly helping Team USA win the finals in that event as well.

Beyond getting free gear and visiting a new country, Jack would never forget the 2019 championships in Budapest. He had long dreamed of wearing the USA flag on his cap and competing for his country in an international meet, and Junior Worlds was his first (of hopefully many) to represent the red, white, and blue.

Similar to Michael Marsh's time at the 1993 World Championships, Jack's experience at Junior Worlds was a memorable one. From the cameras and lights to the music and cries of spectators, both international competitions closely mirrored one another. And while Jack made many mistakes along the way, including going out too fast on his 100 of the men's 4x100m freestyle relay, the Junior World Championships was his first opportunity to represent Team USA, and he was grateful for that experience.

Jack's memory of that competition sparks a contagious excitement as he recalled his teammates and competitors, the facility, and the spectators. As we talked, his humility that surrounded swimming at Junior Worlds surfaced as well. Team USA had initially invited Jack to swim in only one event at that World Championship, and even though he eventually swam in two relays, he recognized that his entire experience at his first international competition, from the gear to the facilities, was a gift.

Before one of my races, as I stood behind the blocks, I got tunnel vision. And I was like, "Holy crap, this is the most beautiful pool I've ever seen."

As Jack continued to describe his experience in Budapest and at the Danube Arena, I became increasingly curious about how he responded to the pressure of being at a meet as intense and high stakes as Junior Worlds. And because rewriting the conversation with my own words would take away from its authenticity, here is a condensed snippet from our conversation as we discussed the athlete's response to pressure:

Olivia Barnes: *So different athletes handle pressure differently. Whenever some of us get under too much pressure, we let it get inside our head and will flunk out or bomb our races. Others use it as a sort of fuel or just try to ignore it until the race or game or whatever is over. But how do you handle pressure?*

Or what would you say is your mechanism for coping with pressure?

Jack Armstrong: *Well, I hope I have the pressure before the meet starts because I thrive under pressure. I love being under pressure because it just fuels me, which was probably one of the things that helped me when I was racing for Team USA. There is pressure to perform for my country out there. I was like, "Oh my goodness, I need to perform." The pressure was great, and I enjoyed it.*

The pressure is not so great, however, whenever you're not having a great meet. Like whenever you're talking to your friends behind the blocks and you're telling them what you're going to go, and then you just bomb your race. Then you're like, "Holy crap, the rest of this meet is going to be so embarrassing." Yeah, so pressure is good when you're confident. And if the confidence matches the pressure, it's a recipe for success.

Olivia Barnes: *So how do you manage your confidence so that you don't let the pressure overwhelm you? Because I know that our coach has talked a lot about how, if an athlete has a bad race at the start of the meet, it is important to let it go. So how do you manage your confidence if you have a bad race at the beginning of the meet? And how do you try to push the bad races aside and keep it from determining the rest of the meet?*

Jack Armstrong: *Well, I try to break down the race, see, like what went wrong. And could this have been a* *good race? I mean, if it couldn't, that's just unfortunate. But I try to break it down, see what could have been improved and what couldn't have been improved on. And if there are enough things that could have been improved on, then it means that I'm having a good meet; I just didn't have a good swim. And then in the following days of the meet, I find and try to nail those ratios and see what happens.*

Our conversation continued as we began to cover the intensity and atmosphere of different competition environments, such as collegiate dual meets, club, and international swim meets, but one thing that really stuck out to me was Jack's intentionality around his mental readiness and strength leading up to and during competitions. External pressure gives Jack the fire to perform well, but interestingly, the self-induced pressure trips him up the most.

Jack has a way to go before he has mastered these ratios of pressure and confidence perfectly, but similar to Michael Marsh, Jack is aware that to be truly an accomplished swimmer, both the body and the mind need to be strong. And along with his understanding around mental health, Jack also highlighted a point many athletes fall trap to—letting the sport define the athlete. He said:

Athletes, they finish their sport and they realize that they have nothing else in life because they gave it all to their sport. They have nothing, and they don't know what their purpose is. I believe it is good to just take a step back from the sport. Take a step back, go outside, and stand barefoot in the grass.

Jack's swimming career has been far from simple. With constant ups and downs, the path he took to become the athlete he is now probably looked a bit like a roller coaster and probably felt like one too. But through patience, hard work, and intentionality he has shown and described in practice, meets, and in our interview, I can't wait to see where Jack's athletic career goes from here.[1]

RECAP

CHAPTER OBJECTIVES

Answering the questions from Behind the Minds of Athletes:

- What went through Jack Armstrong's mind before, during, and after the men's 4x100 meter freestyle relay at the 2019 Junior Worlds?
  - Before the race, Jack focused on the excitement that came from his first international competition.
  - During the race, Jack focused only on doing the best he could for Team USA and the rest of his relay.
  - After the race, Jack focused on how grateful he was to have competed in that relay.
  - This was a healthy race. Even though he did not follow a racing plan, Jack was mentally and physically prepared.
- How did those responses compare with the men's 100-meter freestyle at the 2018 Nationals?

---

1   In the summer of 2021, Jack competed at the American Olympic Trials and placed 25th overall. He is now in the top ten fastest collegiate sprinters in the country.

- Contrasting his Junior Worlds race, Jack primarily focused on just trying to make the American Junior Worlds team.
- Contrasting his Junior Worlds race again, during the race, Jack focused on how discouraged he was that he was not swimming as fast as he could.
- Contrasting his most exciting race again, Jack focused on using his race as fuel to do better next time.
- This was a mental game. Jack was prepared physically, but the mental pressure from his desire to make it to Junior Worlds affected his performance.
- And how did Jack respond to and handle the pressure that came from being on a highly competitive stage?
  - Jack understood that the mind played a critical role in his performance and, therefore, engaged with the external pressure and tried to use it to build confidence and excitement.
  - Jack also understood that in order to keep meets from snowballing into disaster, it was essential to look at each individual race from a level-headed perspective and stable mental state.

KEY TAKEAWAYS:
- Do not let the **negative outcome** of one event define the outcome of the following ones.
- **Mental** and **physical strength** are both necessary for high-quality performances.
- Also…speed is like a **butterfly**.

CHAPTER 4

ELIZABETH BEISEL

———

"Between peaks there are always valleys.
How you manage your valley determines
how soon you reach your next peak."

—SPENCER JOHNSON

ELIZABETH BEISEL

The cover of the book was black and white.

A woman's smiling face stared up at me from the glossy page. Her hair, tossed over her shoulder, was wet, as if she had just emerged from the pool, and her eyes sparkled with excitement, mischief, and beauty. I had dreamed of reading this book for months, and now it was finally in my hands.

I opened the book and began to flip through the pages, scanning the chapters and catching random words here and there: Stanford University… Nationals… Melbourne… violin. Suddenly, a sentence jumped out at me. Sticking my thumb in as a placeholder, I stopped my continuous flipping of pages and opened the book wide. Beginning from the top of the page, I searched for the phrase that had caught my eye. And then I found it. In little black letters that stood out brighter from the rest against the off-white page, it read:

"I won the 200 backstroke at eleven years old, the youngest Junior National Champion ever."

I stared at the page for a long time. I barely grasped the gravity the sentence held and was *completely* shocked. I probably couldn't have even done a single *push-up* at eleven years old, much less break records and win gold medals while competing against athletes three to seven years older than I was.

I could barely wrap my head around that statement; it seemed too impossible. My heart pounded with excitement and wonder as I held the book in my shaking hands. I had no idea how to react, but after several moments of staring, I finally found words again. And my response? It was simply, *WOW!*

That athlete is none other than two-time Olympic medalist, three-time Olympic swimmer Elizabeth Beisel.

In my dictionary, the words Elizabeth Beisel carry significant weight. I remember cheering for her in both the 2012 and 2016 Olympic Games, and I remember celebrating as she stood on the podium for her first Olympic medal in her 400 IM. The blonde swimmer in the black USA cap with BEISEL written in bold white letters on the side was not simply a member of Team USA in my mind, but a true inspiration.

Elizabeth's dedication and effort within the pool and her leadership outside of it were evident through her countless races and performances. Even though I rarely swam Elizabeth's signature races—the 200 back and 400 IM—she motivated me to train harder, work diligently, and trust the process so that one day, I might follow her footsteps and compete in a future Olympics. So naturally, when I found out she had written a book that highlighted her athletic journey, analyzed the good parts and the bad, and demonstrated her leadership, I was eager to read it.

While the first sentence I read from her book, *Silver Lining*, filled me with wonder, it did not take long to realize that the *entire* book would have the same effect. From cover to cover, it only took me a weekend's worth of reading to finish. And while I will admit that I am a big reader and have always loved spending hours on end within the written world of books, *Silver Lining* instantly engaged me with Elizabeth's story and captivating words.

Since I was a competitive swimmer myself, and an Olympic hopeful, the book resonated with me. Aside from training motivation and competition advice, the most interesting thing about the book was how effectively Elizabeth pulled the reader into what she experienced throughout the whole of her swimming career. Through the painful and beautiful patterns of life, Elizabeth shares her unique experience, weaving an intricate story from various moments where she was on top of the world and moments where she felt the complete opposite.

Through stories and interviews, I have begun to grasp a little more clearly how athletes respond to pressure, prepare themselves physically and mentally in training, and engage in competition. Elizabeth does an excellent job of highlighting her own mental and physical experiences in *Silver Lining*, but because I cannot put her entire book into this one (for that would be a major act of plagiarism and ridiculously unnecessary), I will describe what went on in Elizabeth's mind during some of her key races and competitions instead.

Elizabeth's swimming journey began when she was six years old. In truth, her love for the water was first exposed during the Mommy and Me swimming classes she took as an infant, but her competitive career didn't ignite until a sunny day in the late summer months of 2000. A young Elizabeth sat in her living room staring up at the television with awe as the swimming session of the 2000 Olympic Games began. Excitement flooded through her as she realized she was about to witness her first Olympics ever. And as she stared into the screen as world-class swimmers from all over the globe raced for gold, an idea began to form in Elizabeth's mind. As she watched the athletes swim up and down the pool with blazing speed, celebrating their victories at the finish, and representing their respective countries with pride, Elizabeth realized that she, too, wanted to be part of that experience.

With a quick Google search, Elizabeth found a statistic that stated only 0.0065 percent of people become US Olympic swimmers, but those odds couldn't shake the idea out of Elizabeth's head. And in that moment, the idea solidified. With undeniable determination and an unbreakable spirit,

Elizabeth knew that one day, she would make it to the Olympics, represent Team USA, and earn a gold medal for her country.

For those who are unfamiliar with Elizabeth's athletic career, spoiler alert, she could never reach her dream of winning an Olympic gold medal. Yet her story has a silver lining too because she *did* win countless Junior National, National, and World Championship titles along her long and winding path through elite sports, eventually becoming the first woman to compete for Team USA for twelve consecutive years, and later the leader of the Team USA swim team at her last Olympics in Rio. Competing all over the globe and racing the fastest people in history, Elizabeth gave her all to the sport, and although she might not have an Olympic gold, she has a much more powerful and inspirational legacy instead.

While each of her meets and competitions might be memorable in their own way, one of the most striking competitions in Elizabeth's career was her first Nationals. Elizabeth had attended Junior Nationals in the years previous, consistently returning as a champion in the races she considered her specialties. Although the competition at those meets was fierce, competing at Nationals gave the word "intensity" a whole new meaning.

From traveling across the entire country to competing with and against swimming legends Natalie Coughlin, Michael Phelps, and Ryan Lochte, an appropriate amount of fear and excitement flooded through Elizabeth as she arrived at the competition. Being only thirteen years old, countless athletes who were older, bigger, and generally more seasoned surrounded her. Similar to her first Junior Nationals, Elizabeth was by far the youngest contestant present, but very much *unlike* Junior Nationals, Nationals was open to all ages. People anywhere from three to even twenty years older than she was walked along the pool deck and swam within the warm-up pool. From appearances only, Elizabeth looked completely out of place.

Elizabeth only hoped to make it to finals, not expecting to be exceptionally competitive against the best in the country. After they announced the prelim results, an uncomfortable pounding began in her chest, sending anxiety through her body until her hands shook. She had finished *first* in prelims. She might have looked out of place on the pool deck, but in the water, she *thrived*.

For the rest of the day, anticipation coursed through her body as doubt and questions flashed across her mind. Could she perform? Did she deserve this number one spot? What if she blew the race and let down not only herself but also her coach, team, and family?

Fear overwhelmed her, but right before the finals of that race began, her coach pulled her aside.

He did not provide her with words of encouragement or sugar-coated support, just honesty, with a slight touch of inspiration. Reminding her of a conversation they'd had earlier in the competition, her coach simply stated: "You are going to make Pan Pacs tonight."

The Pan Pacific Championship was a highly competitive international meet that would take place later that summer. Qualifying hadn't even been on Elizabeth's thirteen-year-old radar. But now it was. So with that in mind, Elizabeth entered the pool alongside the other seven finalists, grabbed the blocks, and raced her first National finals.

As soon as she began swimming, the anxiety she had felt earlier faded away. But even so, Elizabeth writes that to this day, she has no memory of what went on during that race. Her only recollection of the event was when she miscounted her strokes, finishing the race instead by banging her head against the wall. But as she looked up at the scoreboard, she found her name, then her time, then her place.

Next to her name and time was a bright, white number two. She had gotten second place at her first Nationals, and at thirteen years of age, Elizabeth had the opportunity to compete for Team USA at her first international competition.

Elizabeth had long been the odd man out. From a young age, her older teammates, because of her incredible speed and her ability to consistently perform and compete well, had constantly ostracized her. Unfortunately, this feeling stayed with her as she got ready to compete with Team USA at Pan Pacs later that summer. From the post-race interviews to the team meetings, Elizabeth felt alone. Not only was she much younger than all the other members of Team USA, but she also did not know anybody there. She felt separated both physically and emotionally, and all the joy and excitement from placing second in the 200 back and earning a ticket to Pan Pacs slowly began to seep away.

The meals and downtime were the hardest for her—having no one to talk to and no friends for support. But all the loneliness and painful solitude ended one day when one of her Olympic idols, Natalie Coughlin, sat down across from Elizabeth and introduced herself.

Elizabeth was so grateful for Natalie's friendliness, and from then on, Elizabeth knew someone was rooting for her. Someone knew her name and would cheer for and support her, no matter her age. After that short but impactful interaction with Natalie, Elizabeth knew the meet would go well. And it did. Placing second in prelims of her 200 back, and placing fifth in finals, Elizabeth blew away expectations once more by not only achieving a new personal best but also qualifying for her first World Championships scheduled in Melbourne, Australia, a year later.

During her career, Elizabeth struggled with several injuries (including competing with broken ribs and later a broken finger as well), along with struggles in her first years in college and post-Olympic depression. Like Michael Marsh, she used each of those opportunities to learn and grow. Whether using her injuries (both sport and recreational) to fuel her desire to work hard and win, learning from her collegiate mistakes by enforcing strict discipline into her schedule, preparing herself mentally for high-stake competitions, or supporting those who might also struggle with post-Olympic depression, Elizabeth was extremely intentional about using the downs in her career to make her ups even more impressive. Along with treating her failures as learning opportunities, Elizabeth did not lose sight of how far she had come or where and why her journey had flourished as much as it had.

In her last Olympics at the 2016 Games in Rio de Janeiro, she was appointed as a leader for Team USA's Olympic swim team. Taking her role with honor, Elizabeth replicated what Natalie Coughlin had done for her ten years prior and committed herself to look out for and support the younger and less experienced swimmers at that Olympics. Elizabeth's desire to lead has impacted many lives, and from inspiring young swimmers around the world to simply upholding the Olympic athletes, win or lose, as they exited the pool, her journey has been an exceptional one, to say the least.

Elizabeth's wisdom around competing, training, and simply living has packed her book, *Silver Lining,* full to the brim. She constantly emphasized the importance of trust and respect of coaches, teammates, and competitors; highlighted the need for community support; and demonstrated the power of patience, hard work, and passion. Through it all, Elizabeth's *humility* and *gratitude* remained constant.

"Progress is sometimes very slow and gradual, so it can be easy to take how far you've come for granted."
—ELIZABETH BEISEL

This quote is not only beautiful and true, but it perfectly summarizes Elizabeth's mental and physical athletic journey. In some areas of the sport, her progress was effortless, and in others, it was extremely painful, but through it all, Elizabeth endured and remained vigilant of how far she had come. From being a three-time Olympian and two-time Olympic medalist to being an incredible leader both on the pool deck and beyond, whenever Elizabeth looked back on her life, she writes she would not have changed anything. Maybe she didn't get an Olympic gold, and maybe she didn't fulfill her dream in its entirety, but the silver lining is that she worked hard, journeyed far, and achieved the extraordinary.

And for that, she will be remembered.

RECAP

CHAPTER OBJECTIVES:
Answering the questions from Behind the Minds of Athletes:

- What went through Elizabeth Beisel's mind before, during, and after the finals of the women's 200 backstroke at her first Nationals?
  - Before the race, Elizabeth focused on her coach's advice.
  - During the race, Elizabeth focused on swimming her best.
  - After the race, Elizabeth focused on her exciting and extraordinary performance.
  - This was *almost* a mental game. Elizabeth was prepared, but without her coach's support, her nerves almost overwhelmed her.
- How did those responses compare with the women's 200 backstroke at Pan Pacs?[2]

---

2   This was *not* Elizabeth's most disappointing race; nonetheless, it reinforces the idea that without community support, Elizabeth would not have been fully mentally prepared and would not have done as well as she did.

- Contrasting Nationals, Elizabeth focused on how grateful she was to have Natalie's support.
- Like her race at Nationals, Elizabeth focused on swimming her best.
- Similarly again to her race at Nationals, Elizabeth focused on the excitement from her performance.
- This was also *almost* a mental game. Elizabeth was again prepared physically, but without Natalie's support, she would not have been mentally ready to race.
- And how did Elizabeth respond to and handle the pressure that came from being on a highly competitive stage?
  - Elizabeth used her support group of friends, teammates, and coaches to help maintain a healthy mindset and keep the pressure from overwhelming her.
  - Elizabeth also understood that to stay mentally healthy throughout her swimming career, it was important to stay humble about her achievements and grateful for every aspect of the journey.

KEY TAKEAWAYS:
- **Community support** is a vital aspect of success.
- Expressing **humility** and **gratitude** can make the journey much more enjoyable.

PART 1 - BEHIND THE MIND SUMMARY:
Within Behind the Mind, I viewed three separate athletes, using the stories and interviews of each to best capture the behaviors and mentalities of those who participate in elite competitions. Whether through my interview with Mr. Mike Marsh that highlighted the differences of mindsets during his best and worst races, through my conversation with Jack Armstrong, where he reviewed techniques to respond

to intense pressure, or through the stories of Elizabeth Beisel that demonstrated the importance of community, these athletes provided not only quality athletic wisdom but also insight into the depths of what goes within the minds of elite athletes.

PART II

THE MENTAL GAME

CHAPTER 5

DEFINING MENTAL HEALTH

—

Victoria Garrick calls it the hidden opponent.

The American Psychiatric Association calls it a health condition involving changes in emotion, thinking, or behavior (or a combination of those).

I call it a rain cloud on the path of life.

Most people know what it feels like to walk in the rain. They know what it feels like to be soaked to the bone, to be bruised by the heavy droplets, and to be battered by the stinging winds. They know how it feels when the rain seeps into their shoes and their socks suck up enough water to last a lifetime. But they also know what it feels like to make it back home.

Most people know what it feels like to dry off and get warm. They know what it feels like to watch the storm from the window with a cup of tea in their hand, waiting for the sun to return.

I say that mental illness is a rain cloud on the path of life because almost everyone experiences it. Just like with rain, a cloud of depression, anxiety, stress, or something else will catch almost everyone over the course of their lifetime.

Unfortunately, though, very few people see *any* type of mental illness as I do. Often, we categorize people as weak, crazy, or ill when we diagnose them with a mental health issue. These stigmas around mental illness are seriously misplaced. When we look at the definition of *physical* illness, it is very much like that of *mental* illness, yet having a physical illness, even a serious one, has no stigma around it. Rationally speaking, it should not make sense for one type of injury to be considered worse in society than another. But these stigmas are ingrained in our societal interactions.

Working through a mental health issue can be a scary, confusing, and lonely process, but pushing back on the cultural norms that ostracize those who struggle with mental illness is vitally important. I can understand how challenging it is simply to uproot this idea ingrained in our society, so it might be helpful to define the problem in a different way.

Because of the sensitivity around mental health issues and the term *mental illness* specifically, I would like to examine the term mental health instead. Some might define mental health as the absence of mental illness or the presence of a stable emotional state, but I would like to view mental health through another lens.

In an interview between education expert Matthew Barnes (who also happens to be my dad) and emotional and mental well-being expert Fabienne Vailes, Fabienne questioned Matthew on his views around mental illness in the field of education. Fabienne brought up a stark difference in the use of those terms between the American and French/British cultures. Referring to American culture, Fabienne emphasized that "mental health is viewed [in society] as mental *ill*-health." Matthew agreed with her, acknowledging that the term *mental health* is only used when describing some type of disorder or dysfunction. She talked about how, instead, in the culture in which she was raised, mental health was viewed as a spectrum between health and illness. Just like with physical health, mental health is a range, going from one extreme of supernatural health to the other extreme of serious illness that everyone is a part of.

On this mental health spectrum, you have every possible scenario, from people like Viktor Frankl—who have incredible control over their minds and emotions (like the mega-fit individuals on the physical health spectrum)—to people who have more critical mental illnesses (like individuals with broken bones or physical impairments). The term *mental health* does not imply weakness, nor should it trigger unease. It is simply a range that everyone is a part of, and as we all try to strive for better health, both physically and mentally, I hope we can begin to release the stigmas surrounding the terms mental health and mental illness in our world.

"Mental health problems don't define who you are. They are something you experience. You walk in the rain and you feel the rain, but, importantly, YOU ARE NOT THE RAIN."

—MATT HAIG

As we journey to learn more about mental illness, it is important to keep this idea of mental illness and the spectrum that Fabienne brought to light at the forefront of our minds. Both Matt Haig's and Fabienne Vailes' words were wise, powerful, and lasting, and because of their unbiased and honest insight, I internalize the definition of mental health as an experience and a spectrum whenever I hear, read, or speak about anything related to the health of the mind.

Over these next four chapters, I will explore mental health and the stigmas that surround it in athletic communities. Raising awareness about the severity of these stigmas, I invite a more open and honest conversation about athletes and mental health struggles. I will also strive to change the language that surrounds athletes who struggle mentally, which will not only help improve the health of the athletes themselves but will also strengthen the sports community in the process.

CHAPTER 6

STIGMAS AND SHAME

———

Mental illness is a silent pandemic that has swept and continues to sweep across our society. Almost like a noiseless wildfire, it crosses all borders and boundaries, inhabiting almost every community, burning its way through our social networks and interactions. It seems inescapable. It feels like there is nowhere its flames haven't licked.

Around one in every *five* people suffer from some type of mental health issue each year. And although the severity of the mental illness varies between individuals, the fact remains that a *significant* portion of the human population suffers from a mental health issue. But while many people might suffer, very few of those people seek help. The fire of mental illness burns silently because of the overpowering weight of stigmas and shame.

I previously brought to life a new way to look at the touchy term *mental health*. So now that we have reframed how we think about mental health, I would like to explore *why* these stigmas are present and *how* their presence negatively impacts those who struggle with mental health issues.

As defined by the Merriam-Webster Dictionary, stigmas are the marks of shame or discredit. But regardless of how strong or weak they might appear, they can have profoundly powerful effects on those who are the victims. So why are stigmas so present in our culture, even though they can be undeniably harmful? I have one answer for you: ignorance.

The stigmas around mental illness have persisted for as long as they have for many reasons, but ignorance can be the most potent. This is because those who are uninformed and uneducated about the truth around mental health are much more likely to act in a way that has serious negative impacts simply because they are unaware of the gravity of the situation. Ignorance is merely not knowing, but it can still lead to disastrous results.

"Either America will destroy ignorance, or ignorance will destroy America."

—W.E.B. DU BOIS

Part of why those stigmas are so powerful is because they are based on partial truths but grounded in ignorance. Stigmas usually have *some* legitimacy, but exaggerated material and information distort that truth into almost a tool of harm. For example, the idea that people who struggle with mental illness are mentally ill *is* a truth, but the idea that their illness makes them uncontrollably crazy, incompetent, dangerous, disgraceful, and unwanted gives the stigmas such destructive power.

An article published by *EMBO Reports* states that "in cases of mental illness, stereotypes can become dysfunctional because they typically activate generalized rather than customized response patterns; contradictory information can even reinforce stereotypes as 'exceptions prove the rule.'"

And while some people *definitely* have mental health issues serious enough that employment isn't possible and hospitalization might be the only solution, the percentage of people with severe mental health issues is incredibly small and in no way justifies an entire cultural stigma around mental illness.

A staggering 51.5 million people in the US alone struggle with a mental illness, but only 5 percent of all Americans actually struggle with a *serious* mental health issue, such as schizophrenia, bipolar disorder, or major depression. But even if 51.5 million people struggled with a serious mental illness, this stigma around mental health would still be undeniably inappropriate.

Through my research, I have discovered that although many types of stigmas might exist, the two dominant themes of stigmas that surround people with mental illness are,

1. The "You Are Crazy" Stigma
2. The "You Are an Attention-Seeker" Stigma

The *You Are Crazy* stigma is probably the most widely held stigma around mental illness. It is generally seen as the active or passive isolation of people with mental health illness because they are assumed to be psychotic and dangerous.

This stigma is often used against people with very visible, severe, or serious mental health issues.

The other primary stigma is the *You Are an Attention-Seeker* stigma. Although it is not as often thought about, it is equally as powerful, if not more, as the *You Are Crazy* stigma. This stigma is largely present with mental health issues that are not externally visible or serious. It is the assumption that if the mental illness victim is not *seriously* struggling, then they fabricated their pain (and faked their diagnosis) for attention. Both stigma themes are extremely potent, and they trigger isolation, shame, and serious emotional strain.

According to the National Alliance on Mental Illness, suicide is the second leading cause of death of people ages ten to thirty-four in the US. This statistic is as inexcusable as it is horrifying. And because of the severity of this problem, I no longer think about how upending the stigmas around mental health might make me uncomfortable. I think only about the lives lost because we as a society refuse to address this stigma around mental health and the ignorance in which it is rooted.

Now that we understand *why* the stigma around mental health exists, it is time to start unraveling that ignorance by exploring *how* those stigmas affect those who struggle with mental health issues.

One reason the stigmas around mental illness are so powerful is that they affect so many people. And because very few people seek help for their mental struggles, this can have cascading effects. Clearly, the burden of both having a mental illness and living through those stigmas has driven victims of mental illness to try to suppress or ignore the pain. But like a stopper in a volcano, one can only plug mental health issues up for so long before the internal strain pops the cork. In many cases, popping the cork can be fatal.

A while ago, I had the pleasure of interviewing a friend about this very topic. For the sake of her identity and her story, I will keep her as anonymous as possible. As we talked, she described a very memorable experience she had around mental health during her time as a collegiate athlete. Unfortunately, her experience was memorable for all the wrong reasons.

It was a seemingly normal day at practice when one of the women on my friend's swim team began acting oddly. Barely able to support herself, the woman was struggling to swim, and on a Division 1 team, an incompetent swimmer was a sight that was *never* seen. Shocked by this occurrence, the coaches and fellow swimmers watched in confusion.

Eventually, the swimmer was struggling so much that the sports med team had to assist her out of the water, dragging her from the pool because she was unable to get out on her own. The team did not know what was going on or what to make of it. From the water and the pool deck, they watched in horror as their friend and teammate had to be rescued.

Eventually, they learned the swimmer had suffered from a severe overdose from prescribed anxiety and depression medications. It was a very traumatic experience for the entire team, but especially so for my friend, who witnessed *two* more overdoses from her struggling teammate throughout their time in college together.

Recollecting the painful memory, she shared that although she knew that her friend was struggling mentally, she had no idea the extent of the pain. And although we will never know for sure the leading cause of those three overdoses, my friend now knows that if the support system for athletes with mental struggles had been stronger, her friend might have felt more comfortable seeking help before her pain reached an extreme.

Though this story is heartbreaking and tragic, it is only one example of many of the impacts that stigmas can have on people who are struggling with a mental illness but don't feel comfortable being open about their need for help. It pains me to acknowledge that such a large percentage of our population is constantly shunned by the rest because of their struggles.

While I have no idea the full extent of how this woman struggled through suicidal thoughts that resulted in *three* overdoses in college, I do know that the shame and stigmas that surrounded her after her struggles became known were strong and powerful. And whether it is institutional stigmas or public stigmas, the idea that people with mental illnesses are considered disgraceful and disappointing is unfortunately *not* a novel concept—neither is the idea that people who are consistently shamed by those around them begin to shame themselves. This makes the stigma so powerful. One discriminatory comment or gesture can lead to ripple effects, it can lead to shame and self-isolation, and it can lead to needless pain and suffering.

In addition to isolation and feelings of shame, people with mental illnesses become susceptible to physical illnesses as well. People with a mental illness like depression have a 40 percent higher risk of developing cardiovascular and metabolic diseases than the general population. And people with serious mental health issues are nearly two times as likely to develop those illnesses. These stigmas around mental illness are *not* a trivial matter. They are strong and powerful and dangerous. And they can ignite a shame that is hard to erase.

> "Shame: the intense painful feeling or experience of believing we are flawed and therefore unworthy of acceptance and belonging."
>
> —BRENÉ BROWN

Shame can be a land mine. Whether triggered by external situations and individuals or self-imposed, it can be long-lasting and have profoundly negative impacts on those who suffer from it. Shame is a painful emotion caused by the consciousness of guilt, shortcoming, or impropriety. It is a pit full of dark thoughts and slippery walls that makes escape almost impossible. It is deeper than guilt.

Vulnerability and shame expert Brené Brown dedicates an entire chapter in her book, *Daring Greatly,* to understanding and combating shame. She talks about the power of having conversations around shame, how to differentiate shame from other negative emotions, and how different people respond to shame. Her wisdom and expertise shine bright throughout her book. As she helped me understand the value of vulnerability and the danger of shame, I realized that part of its power is that many people who struggle with it are often overlooked or ignored. Similarly, those who shame others often have no idea how much weight their words carry.

Shame is dangerous because it is self-imposed, even if indirectly. Once a person starts sliding into a pit of shame, external forces are no longer necessary to cause injury. Even for people who have begun climbing away from the grips of shame, sometimes the smallest and seemingly most random triggers can reignite that shame within them. But one of the most important reasons shame is so impactful is because shame within one person can create ripple effects throughout communities. Just like the phrase "hurt people, hurt people," if one person falls victim to the shaming from mental health stigmas, the pain will not necessarily stop there.

Throughout her chapter on shame, Brené Brown encouraged people to challenge their shame and bring the shame and vulnerability conversation to light. Often, when we think about the word vulnerability, we see it in a negative context. But just as Fabienne Vailes helped reframe how the term *mental health* is viewed, Brené Brown has created a new way to look at the term *vulnerability.*

Instead of vulnerability being seen as weakness or instability, Brené points out that while "vulnerability is the core of shame and fear and our struggle for worthiness, it appears that it's also the birthplace of joy, of creativity, of belonging, of love."

An honest conversation about mental health requires courage and vulnerability, but it is vitally important to the individual struggling with shame. Shame flourishes in the dark, but with conversation, this can change. It also can create a positive ripple effect of change, helping not only individuals but also the communities who fall victim to mental health shaming and stigmas.

From her 2012 TED Talk titled *Listening to Shame*, Brené Brown emphasized that "we have to talk about shame. And if we're going to find our way back to each other, we have to understand and know empathy because empathy's the antidote to shame. If you put shame in a petri dish, it needs three things to grow exponentially: secrecy, silence, and judgment. If you put the same amount in a petri dish and douse it with empathy, it can't survive. The two most powerful words when we're in struggle: me too."

Before anything else, the shame caused by these stigmas and blatant ignorance around mental illness needs to be disrupted. And although I understand that change can be uncomfortable at times, the refusal to be open to learning about mental health issues is not an option.

And in the wise words of William Pollard, "To change is difficult. [But] to not change is fatal."

As a society, we *must* become comfortable talking about mental illness, reaching out and supporting those who are struggling, and trying to shape a world where the casualties caused by mental health issues become history.

CHAPTER 7

THE WEIGHT OF GOLD

——

As a critical point of entertainment for modern America, sports have become a *huge* part of the childhood of many American youth. From the appeal of athletic greatness to the desire to become a physical phenomenon, kids all around the country, whether in their backyard or for their school or club team, play sports.

While some use sports as only a means of exercise, others pursue it with rigor, striving for elite competition. No matter the driver or prime motivation, training centers, gyms, courts, etc., are present all over urban environments, providing easy access to exercise. Basketball courts, even if not high quality, are located at gyms, some parks, and even many schools, making physical activity readily available. This convenient access to athletic facilities and exercise locations allows people like my parents and grandparents, who no longer play sports, to take pride in staying physically active.

Not only is frequent exercise great for maintaining a healthy body, but research also shows that it is great for maintaining a healthy mind. Unfortunately though, even though exercise helps *improve* mental health, it does not *prevent* mental health struggles. Everybody—executives, actors, construction workers, doctors, teachers, mothers, fathers, you name it—is susceptible to encountering a mental illness at some point in their lifetime, and athletes are no exception.

While athletes carry the persona of being big, strong, competitive, and fierce, the burn of mental illness does not exclude them. While they might show the world that they are void of weakness and tough as nails, data says otherwise.

In the HBO documentary *The Weight of Gold*, Michael Phelps suggests that around **80 percent** of Olympic athletes struggle with post-Olympic depression. And as the 2021 Tokyo Olympics comes to a close, the mental illness statistics within athletic communities have become even more daunting. But Olympic athletes are not the only ones who struggle.

According to an article from Athletes for Hope, professional and collegiate athletes have also shown a shockingly high presence of mental health issues within their respective athletic communities. Around **35 percent** of *all* elite athletes struggle with mental health issues, and for collegiate athletes in particular, only 10 percent of those with mental health conditions seek help.

While training physically in the form of workouts, practices, and meets or games is standard practice for the typical athlete, the maintenance of the health of the mind is not. This is an extreme issue because, for many athletes, not *intentionally* monitoring their mental health will result in mental health issues triggered by increased pressure levels around competitions and games.

Because of the dominant belief and the overwhelming brand that athletes are strong superhero-like people, weakness has become adamantly shunned in sporting communities. Like mold, these mental health issues get worse when hidden, leading to painful outcomes that usually end with a mentally injured athlete. But while I am generalizing a little bit here, it's still true that the desire, almost necessity, to be tough while competing in an elite sport has suppressed many athletes' willingness to come forward, seek help, and be vulnerable to whatever mental struggle they are dealing with. Their stress, anxiety, depression, eating disorders, or any other mental illnesses are kept secret, and many athletes begin to be destroyed from the inside out.

"The body cannot live without the mind."

—MORPHEUS

If athletes do not prioritize the health of their mind as much as they prioritize the health of their body, their performance will be significantly limited and they will risk obtaining an injury in the form of a mental health issue. It is heartbreaking to see so many athletes (many, but not all, women) try to ignore their pain and push through training and competitions only to snap because of years of unaddressed stress, anxiety, depression, or something else.

So does being an elite athlete or competing in highly competitive sports inherently contribute to higher rates of mental illness?

I don't think so. And no research has proven that is the case. But while there is no direct correlation between being a high-level competitive athlete and having a mental health issue, *athletes* are more at risk of ignoring their mental illness. They let it get worse than the typical American because of the specific mental health stigmas around sports communities and the constant necessity to perform well.

Even I, a competitive athlete, but not anywhere close to being elite or professional, experienced the stigma of being an athlete with mental health struggles.

The pressures of athletics can come from many directions, such as from coaches, teammates, parents, supporters, or even athletes themselves. They can take many forms, such as pressure to excel in training or competition, pressure to look a certain way, or pressure to act a certain way.

For me, the pressure was self-directed, and it was a pressure to excel.

I was fifteen years old, had just started my sophomore year of high school, and my life was as busy as it could be. Along with the typical core classes, I was also taking science classes at a local university and, on top of that, was working out three times and swimming anywhere from ten to fourteen hours per week. For all I could tell, I was living the dream: I had dropped a significant amount of time in my key races and was improving rapidly, I was making all A's in my classes, including a high A in my college class, and I was also thriving socially.

The week before my first college test and the day before the swim meet that would determine if I could go to Junior Nationals that winter, all that success went suddenly down the drain.

When I woke up that morning, nothing was unusual. It was Field Day at our school, so my sister and I wore our "house" colors and happily left our uniforms in our drawers. Field Day was one of the most exciting days of the year. They canceled all classes after lunch for the biannual outdoor competition between the four houses of our school, which consisted of various games and events. Although it was a cold and rainy day, nothing seemed to cloud the anticipation of my meet the next day. All I could think about during class was the swim meet, and all I could think about during study hall was my biology test. I could feel my nerves about both the meet and the test settling into my stomach and tying it into a big knot. I desperately wanted to succeed in both, and I wasn't about to let anything get in the way of either.

As our school cafeteria opened for lunch, though, I began to feel a pain in my stomach. Focusing on other things, I quickly dismissed it as pre-race jitters and continued with my lunch. Straight after lunch, the entire school entered Field Day with wild and exciting activities for all to participate in. Conscious of my meet the next day, I intentionally did not exert myself in most of the activities, but as Field Day went on, I began to feel worse and worse. By the end of the day, I felt awful.

Immediately after we got home, I climbed into bed, pressing a pillow to my stomach and praying for the pain to stop.

But it didn't.

That night, my mom took me to the ER because the pain was so bad, I couldn't sleep. And after a sleepless night in the hospital and several more doctor visits, I was told that I had gastritis: the inflammation of the cells lining the inside of my stomach.

Even with medicine, the pain continued for a week. I slept when I could and hardly ate anything. I lost ten pounds in five days. None of my clothes fit the same. But what haunted me the most was not my clothes, or my weight, or the slight lingering pain, but that I had missed both my swim meet and my test. I had blown two prime opportunities to excel, and while I could make up the test later, I had missed my final opportunity to qualify for Junior Nationals.

I felt as if I had failed.

The gastrointestinal doctor told me that increased acid in the stomach triggered by high levels of stress probably caused my onset of gastritis. Although some people in my community waved the idea of a stress-induced physical illness aside, I knew that the combined self-directed pressure of the swim meet and my test and the sudden and seemingly random gastritis were not a coincidence.

I have been much more vigilant about stress since my gastrointestinal incident. Through constant communication with my coaches and self-monitoring, I have lived a much more mentally-healthy and stress-free life. But even though I am part of an athletic community where mental illness stigmas are intentionally challenged and open conversation is encouraged, the pain of the stigmas is still real.

Even writing this story, intentionally trying to demonstrate vulnerability, makes me a little uncomfortable.

For a while, I feared that, as stated by Brené Brown, "'if I shared my shame story with the wrong person, they could easily become one more piece of flying debris in an already dangerous shame storm."

And while my fear was strong, after one of my childhood idols shared his own mental health struggle with the world, I gained the courage to do the same.

Everybody knows the name Michael Phelps. Everyone reveres and respects the power that stands behind his fame. Michael Phelps, the greatest swimmer of all time, an international icon who has inspired millions, the face of American swimming, is a true legend. From his countless remarkable feats, such as attending *five* Olympic Games, setting numerous world records both in individual events and in relays, and being the first to ever win eight gold medals in a single Olympics, Michael Phelps is undeniably a superb athlete, a major influencer, and a phenomenon. But behind that gold-covered, medal-adorned exterior isn't exactly sunshine and daisies.

I remember when I first found out about Phelps' DUI arrest. I was ten years old at the time, and something like that happening confused me. But Michael's struggles with drugs and alcohol are one example of many where athletes struggling with mental health issues try to keep it silenced until it completely overwhelms them.

Depression was Michael's biggest and most consistent mental struggle during and after his swimming career. But instead of trying to go back to a normal life after his second DUI arrest, Michael Phelps intentionally sought help, acknowledging the severity of the problem. With humility and a lot of guts, he turned his struggles into another platform, a platform to help others.

Michael now uses his own struggles and his incredible platform to reach out, advocating for the support of athletes with mental health struggles, like and unlike his own. He has honest conversations around mental illness within athletic communities. As he opens up about his own personal struggles and talks about how he was able to recover and grow into something new, Michael provides a path for athletes all around the world to seek psychological help.

In the HBO documentary, *The Weight of Gold,* directed by Phelps himself, several athletes discuss the challenges that follow their performances at the Olympics. And while advocating for conversation in sporting communities was emphasized, one message that stood out to me clearly was the desire to be seen as human. Even though these athletes are some of the fiercest in the world, they are still human. They still struggle with anxiety and stress just like everyone else, and they still need support when dealing with challenging times. By identifying these elite competitors solely as fierce people, void of weakness, and completed by pure strength and power, we are isolating them at the exact moment when they need community most.

Along with the toxic idea that athletes *have* to perform well is the idea that success is *ONLY* winning the gold, getting the title, or breaking the record. And because our culture has emphasized that success is the only way to be satisfied, athletes all over the world put themselves through extreme physical, mental, and emotional pain to get the gold. Unfortunately, that victory rarely is worth it when the journey is so painful.

And *that* is the true weight of gold, the true weight that comes with striving for greatness on the track, the court, the field, the gym, or the pool. The weight is so heavy that sometimes even a gold medal can't erase the pain of the journey.

The fierceness of athletes is a facade desperately held together by an entertainment industry that makes money off those whose sole purpose is to be big, strong, and fast. Economics has decided what kind of people athletes have to be, not the athletes themselves. And maybe some athletes truly are beasts by nature, in the gym, at work, or at home, but not everyone is that tough, mentally *or* physically. And while it can be fun to perform as if you are the toughest of the tough and show the world you laugh in the face of pain, living an entire life with that appearance is incredibly unhealthy.

Identities have their place, they have their purpose, and sometimes they are very helpful. But identities can also be dangerous. In her phenomenal TED Talk, Chimamanda

Ngozi Adichie shares several examples of the power of a single story and the caution that should be used around viewing anything with only one narrow and limited lens.

"So that is how to create a single story: show a people as one thing, as only one thing, over and over again, and that is what they become."

—CHIMAMANDA NGOZI ADICHIE

For athletes, this single story, or identity, is being strong and fierce and tough. And while Chimamanda highlighted the importance of seeing other people as more than a single story, it is equally important for people to see themselves as more than a single story or an unrealistic identity. The media constantly portrays athletes as fierce, the athletic community celebrates athletes who are the toughest, and the world uses athletes as inspiration to become physically stronger. This single story is so unhealthy and potentially dangerous because, like all single stories, it is not true.

Being an athlete is so much more than a single story. It is more than sweating and screaming at a victory. And it is more than the gold medals won. It is the whole journey, the good and the bad. It is the high points where perfection seems attainable and the really low points when getting out of bed in the morning seems impossible. It is the physical achievements and injuries and the mental ones as well. Having an identity of being tough has its place in sports, but if that identity cannot make room for vulnerability and the courage to be imperfect, then it is a burden more than anything else.

If the classification of "all strength, no weakness" begins to fade, then maybe athletes will become more comfortable opening up about pressing mental health struggles. Maybe they will begin to feel human again, and maybe extreme outcomes of suppressed struggles, like Michael's drinking and drug struggles, will become a rarity. With that hope in mind, it is vitally important to not only embrace conversation around mental health within athletic communities but also to crack the facade that says that athletes *have* to be tough.

What if we could live in a world where mental illness wasn't taboo and people who needed help didn't hesitate to ask? And what if we lived in a world where athletes were humans too, extremely strong humans may be, but humans nonetheless, with fears and struggles just like everyone else? What if the athletic community embraced the struggles of life together, as a team, and sought to *end* the problem of mental health, not suppress it? I wonder what that world would look like for athletes and for everyone else.

CHAPTER 8

IF YOU WANT
TO GO FAR...

———

*"If you want to go fast, go alone. If
you want to go far, go together."*

—AFRICAN PROVERB

When I was young, my dad used to always tell me this proverb. And whether he used it to reverse-psychology me into asking him for help or simply to give me a gold nugget of wisdom I could carry with me forever, I don't know. But I do know that this proverb hasn't left either of our lives.

For my dad, who is big on education and very knowledgeable in that field, community has proven vital to the educational success of children. It takes the intentional support of teachers, parents, family, and friends to help young students and learners grow into educated and successful adults. Unfortunately, on the flip side, my dad has seen, through his work and research, that many children who travel through their educational life alone or with very little support are unable to go as far, metaphorically speaking, as those who *have* a strong community. Thus, they go through life with poorly developed educational readiness.

While education can be applied to the quote above with ease, that proverb has started to speak to me through another lens. For me, community has begun to prove itself essential to the mental health of individuals, and specifically athletes. I previously talked a lot about the mental burdens of high-level athletes and how destructive the stigmas that surround mental health can be.

I highlighted how unfortunately common mental health issues are, using the widely known statistic of "one in every five people" to emphasize that point. In this chapter, I would like to look at the other side of that statistic. So *what about the other four?* If one in every five people struggle from a mental health issue each year, *what about the other four?*

I recently spoke with my friend Amanda Presgraves about sports, mental health, and nature. She had competed and trained for James Madison University, a competitive Division 1 school, throughout her time in college. Although our conversation began around her life as a student-athlete, her unique experiences around mental health within the sport turned the conversation in a different direction.

Amanda had been a highly competitive athlete since the age of four, and when she entered college, that identity remained. As an accomplished competitor, she fit right into her Division 1 collegiate team and quickly formed close bonds with the other women. It was her first year in college, and training, competing, studying, eating, sleeping, and managing her social life (not necessarily in that order) kept her *extremely* busy. Time slipped by in a blur between competitions, tests, and other activities, and in no time, her freshman year was over. And then, after a three-month-long summer break, sophomore year began. Collegiate life had a similar rhythm to her first year in college, but this time, having more experience on how to balance the school, sport, and social aspects of her life, Amanda began to get into an effective and comfortable groove. Training and lifting were going well, her academics were on point, and the friendships she had made the year before began to reignite. But while her life seemed to be going almost perfectly, a sudden injury turned her world upside down.

After tearing both the labrals in her hips, Amanda was told she would have to undergo double hip surgery and might never be able to compete again in her life. Just like that, she was unable to train or compete with her team. Just like that, her lifelong identity of being a highly competitive athlete was torn apart.

As we talked, Amanda described the emotional pain she felt after hearing the news and talked about how important it was for her, and for athletes, to find purpose outside of their sport.

> *Being an athlete is really great for forming a sense of self-efficacy, esteem, and confidence in myself, but it is detrimental when it's taken away. When I speak to athletes now, I always tell them that they're more than*

just an athlete and that is not their only identity. And it's really important for me, and for others, to engage in things outside of the sport as well because that sport can be taken from you at any second. That's what happened to me when I had double hip surgery when I was in college. And I'm so fortunate for that experience now; because before I graduated, I learned that I could do many things besides my sport. I could start businesses, I could care about other things, I could travel the world.

But too often, people that have been an athlete their whole life and who have focused on one sport their whole life, they graduate from college or retire from the sport, and they're like, who am I? What do I do with myself now? What do I care about? And, what's my purpose? And segueing into mental health, that is where a lot of athletes—post-Olympic or post-collegiate athletes in general—begin to get depressed. They lose their sense of identity and purpose in life.

Amanda's immediate response to losing her sport was intense purposelessness. As Jack Armstrong and I both mentioned in previous chapters, being an athlete was the single story Amanda had told herself for so long that the danger of that single story, as Amanda stated, was how it became extremely detrimental to her mental health to have that story taken away.

But Amanda was extremely fortunate because instead of getting sucked into a pit of depression, she stepped aside from the sport while she recovered from her hip injury and explored new things. At the last minute, she decided to join a friend who was part of a study abroad program in the Philippines. She designed her own learning experience with goals of getting scuba certified, visiting rain forests, climbing mountains, and researching the physiology of people in those different natural environments. Suddenly, Amanda realized that she was more than just an athlete, that she had interests in other areas of life, and that she was capable of finding purpose outside of her sport.

After recovering from her injury, Amanda continued competing, and she finished out her last years of college training with her team once more. But even though her life went back to how it had been prior to her hip injury, Amanda had learned her lesson and was intentional about prioritizing a multifaceted identity, one not solely tied to being a competitive athlete.

As we continued talking, Amanda revealed that she was one of the *only* members on her women's collegiate team who didn't suffer from some kind of mental health issue during college. When I asked if her trip abroad was why she never struggled mentally throughout college, she strongly agreed. Because of her injury, she found time to learn how to strengthen her mental health by finding a diverse and healthy purpose in life.

Although her injury and her trip abroad allowed her to grow stronger mentally, the most important lesson was that she did not do it alone. Her community helped her transition from her athletic injury to finding a new identity. It helped her grow strong mentally so she could flourish throughout the rest of her college experience and beyond.

Mental health issues in athletic communities are unfortunately extremely common, and Amanda witnessed her fair share of mental struggles from teammates and fellow athletes. But regardless of the severity of the mental health issue, the importance of community support is a common theme. Research has shown that we desire to connect with others and establish a sense of belonging. Amanda found that sense of belonging when she joined her friend in their international adventure. Even though she had been previously defined as *just* a high-level athlete, she was completely accepted as a member of the study abroad group.

Unfortunately, because of the shame and stigmas surrounding mental health issues within sports communities, very few athletes who struggle internally can find that sense of emotional belonging in their communities. And although from the outside eye, many athletes "fit in" within their respective sports groups, fitting in and belonging are two very different things.

In the wise words of Brené Brown, "Fitting in is assessing a situation and becoming who you need to be to be accepted. Belonging, on the other hand, doesn't require us to change who we are."

And that is where the role of the "other four" comes into play.

The role of the other four, the people who don't struggle with mental illness, is to provide a healthy community for those who struggle with mental health issues. According to the National Alliance on Mental Illness, the three most beneficial aspects of community are **Belonging**, **Support**, and **Purpose**.

Below, I highlight why each aspect is vitally important in athletic communities and show the negative effects that can result from the lack of community.

BELONGING

Using Brené's definition of belonging, very few athletes are so comfortable in their respective athletic community that they no longer feel the need to change who they are in order to be accepted. But not only is there significant emotional ease from being accepted without having to change anything, but truly belonging also promotes vulnerability.

Athletic communities heavily prioritize strength, so an athlete needs a good deal of vulnerability in order to seek psychological help. A powerful community, where they earnestly foster a sense of belonging, helps reduce the fear of being vulnerable.

One of the biggest and most important roles of the "other four" is to make a community where those who struggle with mental health issues can experience that true sense of belonging.

On the flip side, without community, or even with community, but without any sense of belonging, much of the reverse occurs. Athletic communities are, in fact, communities, but because the cultivation of true belonging is not often put into play, increased stress to "fit in" and fear of showing weakness, such as a mental health issue, become very present within the athletes.

And when "fitting in" is valued more than truly belonging, vicious cycles of desperation to fit in and increased mental struggles, on top of the already physically taxing life of competitive athletes, can begin to occur.

SUPPORT

Support is almost as necessary, if not just as necessary, as the sense of belonging within athletic communities. Like belonging, support is knowing there will be someone to lean on even during the worst of times. The reason I said that support is almost as necessary as belonging is because, with a true sense of belonging within a particular community, strong support within that same community is almost inevitable. Support is extremely important for athletes because it gives them a sense of security that even if they are struggling, they will not be isolated or ostracized because of their struggles.

In the Shame and Stigmas chapter, I talked a lot about how often society brutally shuns people who struggle with mental health issues. This isolation frequently occurs in athletic situations absent of genuine community support. And I am not talking about sports psychologists or nutritionists. Although their support and help are critical, without the loving support from teammates, coaches, family, friends, or spectators, the potent stigmas that surround mental illness in athletic circles effectively begin limiting athletes' ability to seek help increasing their risk of developing a mental health issue or worsening their current one.

PURPOSE

The third beneficial aspect of community is purpose. Within healthy communities, not only are belonging and support prioritized, but purpose is also present as well. And just as with belonging, Amanda's story showed the importance of purpose as well.

In the words of the National Alliance on Mental Illness, "In community, people fill different roles, and these roles can give people a sense of purpose through bettering other people's lives. Having purpose, and helping others, helps give meaning to life."

This can apply to athletic communities as well. Whether it is several members on the team who enjoy cooking and are encouraged to share meals with the rest, or it is an athlete who is also a gifted artist and uses their gift to spread beauty, sport communities that embrace the differences and unique gifts outside of the common trait of being an athlete inspire purpose throughout the community.

Amanda Presgraves and Jack Armstrong both emphasized the importance of not tying their single identity to their sport because they understood how devastating it could be for an athlete to lose that sense of purpose when that identity is removed. Purposelessness can lead to compounding negative results that can trigger and worsen mental health issues. Athletic communities often promote identities that focus solely on the sport, and it is essential to the health of the athletes to challenge that mindset and embrace multifaceted and diverse identities that make all of us uniquely human.

Belonging, support, and purpose make communities healthy and long-lasting. Not all communities are blessed with being extremely healthy, but for those who lean more toward the unhealthy side, prioritizing the growth of true belonging, genuine support, and a sense of purpose is a definite step in the right direction.

Through research, stories, and experiences, I have begun to learn how important it is for the "other four" to build healthy communities with and for one another. And while I have tried to reorganize my life to be more intentional about cultivating belonging, support, and purpose within the communities of which I am a part, I never prioritized building a healthy community.

I was a freshman in high school when I met Aspen.[3] She was quiet, a little like me, and we quickly bonded, being one of the few people in our class who had no other connections leading into high school. We met at an event for freshmen and sophomores several weeks before the start of school, designed to help connect the underclassmen. As I walked into that gathering, I was met by several groups of smiling faces and loud talking. While everyone seemed friendly and nice, I was alone and had no one to talk to.

---

3   For the sake of my friend's privacy, I am using the name Aspen as a placeholder.

Sighing inwardly, I made my way to the snack table, putting a couple of slices of pizza on my plate and filling the rest of the empty space with chips. After filling my plate and grabbing a Sprite from the cooler nearby, I turned around and headed back toward the gathering, searching for an empty seat or someone to talk to. But again, everyone seemed to have already been included in their own groups. Spotting an empty seat near the edge of the pool, I made my way to sit down and eat, but before I reached the chair, I noticed a girl.

She was alone like me. She was huddled alone near a wall and had wrapped her arms around her chest and let her hair fall around her face, partially shielding her from view. I smiled. I knew exactly how she felt. Setting my plate and soda down on the poolside chair to save my seat, I approached her.

"It's Aspen, right?" I asked, using her name tag as a guide.

She nodded, then smiled slightly.

I stuck out my hand. "My name's Liv. Do you want to come eat with me? There is pizza over by the fence, and I have a seat right next to the pool if you want to join me."

This time her smile was visible as she shook my hand and agreed to come and sit with me. Her hands were slightly clammy when they touched mine, and little did I know, but her clammy hands would later become an inside joke that would cause us to fall apart with laughter at just the mention of it.

Aspen and I bonded quickly that night, laughing and conversing easily in just a few minutes. At the end of the gathering, we exchanged phone numbers and promised to meet up again on the first day of school. Now, this story might sound like your typical teenage girl BFF origin story, but it breaks my heart to say that our relationship did not remain this strong.

Before school started, we often stayed up late discussing our fears about starting high school, planning our outfits, and trading random stories and experiences. When my alarm rang out to announce my first day of high school, I had no anticipation of what the day, or even the year, might hold. I knew I had Aspen.

The first semester of our freshman year went by like a blur. Aspen and I shared most of the same classes, and before our teachers started assigning seats to the students, we would always grab the same round table in English I or sit across from each other in Pre-AP Biology. Like most friends, we had our disagreements, times where I would say something that would anger her, or the other way around, but we always seemed to find our way back to one another, and we didn't let our differences get the best of our relationship.

Aspen was one of my best friends not because she was cooler than anybody else but because she loved and supported me without fail. From playing games at her house on weekends to dressing up and going to the fabulous all-school musical our high school put on, the first semester of our freshman year of high school was everything I could have ever hoped for. But something changed after Christmas break. Something in our relationship began to unravel, slowly and unnoticeably, until everything seemed to just fall apart.

Aspen struggled with mental health issues in the form of panic attacks and extreme anxiety issues. While I had been aware of her struggles during the first semester, the second semester was the first time I actually witnessed them. It pains me to share how poorly I responded whenever Aspen needed help, but my own mistakes demonstrate just how important it is for the "other four" to maintain a strong and healthy community.

Several times during that semester, Aspen had a panic attack severe enough to have to leave the classroom. Teachers or classmates had to help calm her down in the bathroom. And after each panic attack, I began to distance myself from her a little bit at a time. Eventually, I ignored her panic attacks and struggles with anxiety, letting the other girls in our class help her instead. She was my best friend, and yet whenever she needed me most, I distanced myself and removed my support.

I think I behaved that way for many reasons. First, I completely bought into the **You Are an Attention-Seeker** stigma, which caused me to become increasingly annoyed whenever class was interrupted, delayed, or even stopped because of Aspen's mental struggles. Second, I was afraid. As a fourteen-year-old, I had no idea what to do or what was really going on. I did not understand how painful mental health issues could be or how to help the person who was struggling. But no excuse can justify abandoning Aspen because of her mental struggles.

The story of my relationship with Aspen is extremely important because it highlights how vital community is for those who struggle with mental illnesses. While I definitely did not exemplify the building of a healthy community, our other classmates, who took my place helping Aspen, perfectly demonstrated how crucial reliable and genuine support systems are within communities. Because of the behaviors of our other classmates, Aspen could still belong, feel supported, and have purpose.

I am so grateful that our other classmates did not follow me in isolating Aspen, but instead, taught me by their actions what a strong community truly looks like.

In the words of Coretta Scott King, "The greatness of a community is most accurately measured by the compassionate actions of its members…a heart of grace and a soul generated by love."

I have since apologized to Aspen for how I treated her, but although she forgave me, I know the beautiful and friendly relationship we had at the beginning of our freshman year in high school is no longer possible.

Community can be an extremely powerful support system that can uphold and strengthen people regardless of whether they are struggling mentally. With a strong community, those in need have ample opportunity to develop true belonging, support, and a sense of purpose. Without a healthy community, struggling individuals can become seriously emotionally hurt, like the way I hurt Aspen, and their struggles can worsen.

I desperately wish someone had called me out on my actions then, but I learned a hard lesson, nonetheless. Because of my own personal fear and ignorance, I both hurt and lost one of my best friends. My story with Aspen also proves that although a community can *appear* healthy and strong, the intentionality of prioritizing belonging, support, and purpose during the tough times is *essential* to the community's survival.

Since my relationship with Aspen, I have become much more aware of how important strong communities are. I have become much more intentional about trying to create an environment of belonging, support, and purpose within my swim team and in other areas of my life because I now know how much it matters. Having a strong community is not a one-time thing but a constant struggle and challenge, but by working hard at preserving its health, it will pay off in the end.

Being an elite athlete is far from easy, but together, we can go far. As stated in the quote at the beginning of this chapter, together, it is possible to create environments and communities where athletes thrive both mentally and physically, and not just within their sport but throughout their entire lives. It is my dream that one day those types of communities will become completely normal.

CHAPTER 9

SPEAKING FOR
THOSE UNHEARD

—

The constant flashing of cameras fills the air with blinding light as Vic steps onto the court. Thousands sit in the audience, many more than she's ever played in front of before, and her heart pounds with anticipation, excitement, maybe a little fear, and a lot of adrenaline. It is the first game of the season.

This is PAC-12.

The number four is traced upon her back in a gold emboldened font that stands out against the crimson of her jersey. The entwined letters of 'S' and 'C' are adorned near her left shoulder, representing the University of Southern California.

Although she is playing volleyball with the then-number-one college volleyball team in the country, she still has a lot to prove. As a walk-on with no scholarship, this game means more than just a dream come true. This is her opportunity to prove that she is an underdog no more. Instead, she is an elite Division 1 athlete and an invaluable addition to the USC women's indoor volleyball team.

Today's PAC-12 match is against the athletes of blue and gold: the UCLA Bruins.

Pauley Pavilion is UCLA's home court, and the seats are packed with fans, supporters, and friends. And although drowning out the deafening cheers from the audience and the constant flashing of cameras is a challenge, Vic mentally prepares herself for the game, focuses her mind, and picks up the ball.

She stares across the court, looking at the red and gold backs of her teammates on her side of the court and at the blue and white jerseys of the opposing team through the net. Then she serves the ball.

The game has begun.

Scoring the first point of the match, USC quickly climbed into a lead. Her team is a powerhouse. With several extremely experienced and inspirational players, USC managed to get an impressive nineteen points before UCLA began to make a comeback. But by the end of the first set, USC was still in the lead. The second set starts and finishes with a score of USC 24 to UCLA 12: the women's volleyball team of USC is dominating. And as the third set starts, with a struggle, but an eventual score for USC, Vic begins to wonder: is it possible that her team could sweep UCLA in the first match of the season *and* on UCLA's home court?

Well, she didn't have to wonder for long.

Her first PAC-12 game of the season could not have gone any better. From serving the match's opening ball to serving the game point that got USC their first victory of the season, this game was truly a dream come true. This match was not perfect by any stretch, but it was the first of USC's victories that gave them the number one seed leading up to the NCAA tournament. More importantly, it was *her* first game (of many to come) as a USC Trojan—her first game to represent the red and gold.

This is Victoria Garrick.

Victoria Garrick was born in Chicago but grew up in Atherton, California—south of San Francisco. With her long and wavy sun-bleached blonde hair, Victoria looks like a classic Cali-girl by appearance, yet her compelling and genuine smile, athletic build, and unique experience set her apart.

Like many other high school and teenage girls, Victoria played volleyball growing up, but while some girls played volleyball without much intensity or commitment, Victoria was an elite competitive player. Victoria became an amazing volleyball player, training hard and playing well. Unfortunately, she wasn't amazing enough to get recruited by her dream school, the University of Southern California.

But, in classic Victoria-Garrick-style, Victoria did not let that get the best of her. By consistently emailing and contacting the coaches of USC's women's indoor volleyball team, she was eventually allowed on the team, if only as a walk-on and without a scholarship.

Victoria did not let her walk-on status get the best of her. With very low expectations of her ability to perform, she trained hard and began to prove her competence as a Division 1 athlete.

In her freshman year of college, Victoria blew expectations away by becoming a starter and playing in USC's thirty-six matches that year. To all outsiders, Victoria's first year at USC looked comparable to a Hans Christian Anderson fairy-tale. From her gorgeous and virtually flawless Instagram feed to her outstanding success on the court, and from her rigorous academics to her lively social life, Victoria Garrick was living the *perfect* college experience. For her, life couldn't be better...or could it.

Although her outside might have looked picture-perfect, she was seriously struggling internally.

When Victoria first became a member of the USC volleyball team, it was a dream come true. But, as her college life went on, she realized that she had no idea how much it would cost her. From her full-time academic status to her full-time athletic status, along with many other factors, Victoria began to struggle to find a balance in her life. And with increasing pressure to perform well on the court, in the classroom, and within social events, Victoria's stress level began to rise. It was not long before she began to struggle with anxiety and depression.

Not only were her mental struggles taboo, but Victoria could not find any fellow athletes online who similarly struggled internally. Having no support and feeling stigmatized by her developing internal battles, Victoria's mental health began to worsen.

In a video about her 2020 Speaking Tour, she said, "I was always that person who was excited and wanted to get out there and play my favorite sport and enjoy the experience. Suddenly, that had all changed. I didn't feel like myself anymore. I couldn't snap out of it, and I felt completely alone."

"Sometimes life is too hard to be alone."

—ELIZABETH GILBERT

Victoria's student-athlete journey was so painful that sometimes she fantasized about getting so badly injured that she could just have a break from her jam-packed life of constant traveling, training for volleyball, and studying and test-taking for class.

And on top of all the physical and emotional demands, she also struggled with a mental illness disorder: binge-eating.

But while loneliness, and stress, and extreme pressure threatened to break Victoria Garrick, she, in classic Victoria-Garrick-style, found a way to overcome.

After getting help from a sports nutritionist and a psychologist for her mental health, Victoria knew many other student-athletes like her might still be struggling alone and in the dark. With courage and a lot of vulnerability, Victoria began to speak up about her journey through mental health while being a student-athlete.

"What mental illness needs is more sunlight, more candor, and more unashamed conversation," says Glenn Close, American actress and mental illness activist.

And that is exactly what Victoria did. It was 2017 and her second year of college when Victoria first made her mark by giving a TED Talk at TEDxUSC. Her talk was titled, *Athletes and Mental Health: The Hidden Opponent.*

Applause greeted her as she walked into the spotlight and took her place on top of the red-carpeted circle that marks that stage of so many TED talks worldwide. In a flowy burgundy blouse and black slacks, Victoria's athletic build was apparent as she faced her audience and prepared to speak. She took a deep breath and then began.

> *You have to be at a team lift at 6:00 a.m., but you're accidentally one minute late because you slept through your alarm. Your heart's pounding from sprinting to the gym, but nobody cares that it was because you were up until 2:00 a.m. studying for an exam that you still don't feel prepared for. You can feel the tension between you and your teammates who now have to run sprints tomorrow at 6:00 a.m. because you, she paused for emphasis, were one minute late.*

> *You start the lift and your mind's just not in the right place, but it doesn't matter: you have to lift. And as soon as it's over, you scarf down breakfast on your way*

to an 8:00 a.m. class. And you get there and your hair's still wet because you didn't have time to dry it.

The professor looks at you and says, "Where's the homework assignment?" But you forgot it. How could you forget it? You were supposed to be on top of everything. So you sit there and you worry about what else you might have forgotten. And at noon, you get a thirty-minute break, but it's not really a break because you use it to quickly make up an assignment that you missed for last week's game.

And soon it's 12:10 p.m. And to you, forty minutes does not feel like enough time to get on the court and be ready even though it actually is. So you head over, and at 1:00 p.m., practice is starting, and you have to forget everything that happened in your day because at practice, you have to perform. You can't not perform, she said to the audience as the emotion in her voice rose, because there's someone better than you, someone competing with you, and someone in high school who just committed to be you. So forget the zero on your assignment. Forget the test you're not prepared for. Forget the friends you haven't seen in weeks. Forget the argument you had with your parents. Play well, pass well, perform.

And when it's finally over, you find yourself staring in the locker room mirror trying not to cry. And you ask yourself, Is this how I'm supposed to feel?

There was a long pause as Victoria finished her minute and a half introduction. She stared out at the audience and took a breath. It only took ninety seconds to draw the audience into her life and give them a feel for what a typical day might look like. Their attention was hers. She glanced down, then back up, and continued her speech.

After formally introducing herself, questioning the audience about mental health, and giving a brief description of her experience playing volleyball for USC, Victoria began to get into the meat of her talk: mental health issues in collegiate athletes.

With shocking statistics, Victoria shares that around **30 percent** of 2,100 student-athletes self-reported that they were feeling overwhelmed, according to the results from a 2015 GOALS study of the student-athlete experience. Also, through her own self-conducted survey, Victoria found that a similarly large percentage (**40–60 percent** depending on the question) of student-athletes from colleges all over the country struggled with a mental health issue. The issue of mental illness had not gotten any better two years after the 2015 GOALS study.

Not only was Victoria scandalized by how little conversation was active around the issue of mental illness in athletes, but she was heartbroken by how common it was. To her, those two years between her survey and the 2015 GOALS survey were a sure sign of the need for action around the mental support of collegiate athletes. Those two years signified how little advocacy there was for action and how little motivation there was to change.

Concluding her twenty-minute-long TED Talk, Victoria challenged her audience to speak out on social stigmas such as mental health and encouraged them to be compassionate and supportive of people struggling with mental illness in their individual communities. Victoria was not about to let the conversation around mental health in student-athletes fall silent. From her TED Talk, which now has over 350,000 views, she began finding her voice to raise awareness, make a change, and let fellow athletes know that what they were going through was okay and that she was there for them.

A couple of years later, after rounding out her college experience and volleyball career, Victoria Garrick began touring the country, giving talks at high schools, college campuses, and different locations about the danger of mental health issues in student-athletes. Talking about her own mental experiences as an athlete, the experiences of others, and data to back it up, she began to pave the way for a new stream of positive change. Victoria began to share her journey through college, mental health struggles, and volleyball, helping her fellow athletes overcome mental barriers and issues and inspiring sports communities to prioritize the mental well-being of their athletes.

"Victoria's talk on campus was pretty unifying," said David, a football player at Idaho State University, and one of many student-athletes that attended Victoria's speeches in her 2020 Speaking Tour. "It was the first time where all of athletics came together and someone on our level brought light to something that isn't so easily talked about…. When Victoria came, it broke down a lot of barriers and allowed us to kind of open up and express what we were going through and talk about something that is real and that athletes deal with every day."

Through Victoria Garrick's difficult athletic journey, and her immense courage and vulnerability, athletes who struggle internally have begun to be heard and supported—because, after all, athletes *are* human. The advocacy for the communal mental support of athletes brought Victoria a huge platform to make positive change, and she used it well. But Victoria Garrick is not the only athlete who used her experience as an elite competitor to speak out against mental health stigmas in athletic communities.

The open conversation around mental health stigmas in sports communities is long overdue, and recently, many athletes have begun opening up about their mental struggles. An *Insider* article highlighted several athletes who used their platform as a megaphone to speak out about their mental health issues, their concerns about how the sports community reacts to mental illnesses in athletes, and their desire to upend the stigmas. There was an unnerving similarity between their stories.

Part of the reason Victoria's advocacy and the advocacy of many other athletes is so powerful is because 1) it brings to light how common these mental health issues are within the sports community, 2) it shows athletes follow a stark pattern of struggling mentally, but after feeling the sharp sting of stigmas, avoiding the disclosure of their struggles, and 3) it shows how needed change is.

The stories of these athletes have gained traction and snow-balled (in a positive way) into a movement that can truly make an impact and shift what it means to be an athlete. The momentum that has been made must not slow down. I hope to continue this momentum by sharing more stories of those athletes who are paving the way for mental health advocacy in athletic communities and who inspired me to use my athletic platform to make a change.

ALLISON SCHMITT:

Allison Schmitt, a four-time Olympic gold medalist and a close friend of Michael Phelps, has inspired me for as long as I can remember. While life as an Olympian looked fabulous from my side of the computer screen, on the other side, the reality was that Allison was struggling with depression. After some encouragement from Michael Phelps, who had come out about his own struggles, Allison inspired me yet again and spoke out about what she was going through. Her story emphasizes that having a mental health issue is not a one-time quick fix but a lifelong process. Her continued effort to seek help and push through the struggles has made it easier for other athletes to do the same.

KEVIN LOVE:

Cleveland Cavaliers player Kevin Love is another great example of an athlete using their platform to advocate for change. Struggling with serious depression after breaking his hand twice in one season, Kevin opened up on his whole experience, exposing how difficult it was for him during that time. He also shared how important community was for him and how important it was to know that he was not alone even in the midst of his struggles.

"For me, I guess what I needed was to talk to somebody. For me, what I needed was to know that I wasn't alone. If you're struggling right now, I can't tell you that this is going to be easy. But I can tell you that it does get better. And I can tell you that you are definitely not alone."

—KEVIN LOVE

AMANDA BEARD:

The next athlete whose inspiring story was used as a tool for advocacy is Amanda Beard, another Olympic swimmer and medalist. Amanda's impressive swimming career became widely known when she qualified for her first Olympics at just fourteen years of age and made it to the podium three times while there. Although she had a phenomenal swimming career that consisted of seven Olympic medals (two of which were gold), World Championship titles, and apparent success within the pool, Amanda later revealed that while in the spotlight, she seriously struggled with depression and an eating disorder.

Releasing her autobiography, In the Water They Can't See You Cry, *Amanda brought to light the mental struggles she faced during her swimming career and advocated for change. Her swimming journey continued seventeen years after her first Olympic Games. Even though it brought significant pain and struggling, Amanda used her experience to pave the way for future athletes to avoid experiencing her struggles and instead remain both physically and mentally healthy throughout their athletic careers.*

ABBY WAMBACH:

Like Michael Phelps, US women's soccer player Abby Wambach suffered from drug and alcohol addiction and depression during her time as a competitive athlete. And as her career began to close, the stress and fear of losing her core identity of being an athlete worsened her mental struggles. Abby has since recovered from her addiction, instead using her experience to speak out about mental illness within the athletic community. Being a two-time Olympic Champion, Abby used her incredible platform to make a change. She wrote a memoir, Forward, *that highlighted her struggles while competing and advocated for a different approach to mental health issues in sports environments.*

NAOMI OSAKA:

As I am writing this, it has only been a couple of months since Naomi Osaka stepped into the spotlight of mental health advocacy, and she is already making an impact.

As the current number two tennis player in the world, Naomi has used her fame to speak out about the mental struggles she is currently and has faced in the past as an elite athlete. After being fined for not attending a press conference, Naomi withdrew from the 2021 French Open, later revealing that she had skipped the conference because of her stress and anxiety. She went on to express her concerns about how people reacted to the prioritization of her mental health, using the attention to advocate for a shift in mindset around mental health issues in the athletic communities.

SIMONE BILES:

Simone Biles shocked the world at her first Olympics by blowing away the competition in a way that had never been done before. But at her second Olympics, she shocked the world for another reason. When she entered the Tokyo Olympics, the weight of the world had been on her shoulders to perform, but it was too much. Soon after the Games started, Simone, the reigning Olympic and World champion, pulled out of both the team final and the all-around competition to focus on her mental health. As the face of American gymnastics, the whole world had expected her to dominate. Unfortunately, she received a significant amount of backlash toward prioritizing her mental health over competing. Instead of letting the negative comments and reactions faze her, Simone challenged the stigma surrounding mental health and used her platform as the gymnastics GOAT to inspire change and raise awareness about the mental health struggles of being an elite athlete.

The six athletes above are only a small drop in a great sea of athletes who are currently struggling internally or who have struggled in the past. Still, their vulnerability and courage to come forward and make a change has inspired many, including me, to do the same. A reframe of how mental illness is viewed, approached, and handled in athletic environments is critical to both the success of the athletes themselves and to their long-term mental health—of much more importance than a gold medal or an impressive title.

From people like Victoria Garrick to Michael Phelps and many others, the advocacy for open conversation and erased stigmas around mental health in athletic communities has opened many people's ears and given all athletes voices where they might have been unheard. Athletes, as impressive as they might seem, are vulnerable to mental health issues just like everybody else. Thanks to the leadership of the people above, sports culture is beginning to shift, and their mental struggles are beginning to be seen, free of shame and stigmas, and full of love and support.

And in the words of DeMar DeRozan, NBA player for the San Antonio Spurs, "It's one of those things that no matter how indestructible we look like we are, we're all human at the end of the day."

RECAP

I have been exploring mental illness in the athletic community and how mental health stigmas can seriously negatively affect athletes. And because of the research, stories, and experiences seen, read, and heard about, I have developed a newfound understanding of how potent those stigmas are and how much room exists for positive change.

While my research so far throughout this book has looked at athletes and, more recently, the mental game of athletics, I would now like to shift gears. For those who read the Introduction, or even just the subtitle, to this book, you will know that *Overlapping Worlds* explores how nature can positively affect the mind. So as we begin our journey into the topic of environmental psychology, I would like to ask, how *can* nature positively affect the mind?

PART III

WHAT I CALL
NATURE MAGIC

CHAPTER 10

NATURE AND NURTURE

———

"An understanding of the natural world and what's in it is a source of not only a great curiosity but great fulfillment."

—DAVID ATTENBOROUGH

Nature is not a right. It is a gift.

I will probably *never* understand nature and all its intricacies completely, but as I continue to learn, its wonders continue to amaze me. But before we talk in depth about the wonders of nature, I would like to back up a little.

We all know the phrase *nature versus nurture*, the idea that questions whether an individual's genetics, the environment in which they live, or a mixture of both, influences their behavior and performance. Nature refers to the biological influences involved, and nurture is indicative of how the environment played a role.

But in this chapter, I would like to look at nature through the lens of a different definition. I would like to coin a new phrase with a different meaning: nature *and* nurture. And while the sports version of that phrase refers to athletes, this version refers to the natural world. It highlights how, by shifting the environment to make room for nature, individuals can achieve nature's profound healing powers.

For many, the healing power of nature is self-explanatory. It is intuitive and obvious.

Feeling worn down? Take a trip to the ocean and let the gentle melodies of the waves wash away your fears or troubles. Feeling distracted or scatter-brained? Go visit some mountain ranges and let the wonder of the vast and snowy peaks streamline your mind and focus your thoughts. Craving inspiration? Take a walk through the undisturbed outdoors and let the natural world work its wonders.

But can nature heal people in more tangible ways? Or are the healing effects of being in nature solely a placebo?

Dr. Nooshin Razani is a pediatrician, researcher, and passionate advocate of the healing power of nature. She was one of the first to explore these questions, seeking to understand if nature *could*, in fact, be a prescription to heal.

"The physician treats, but nature heals."

—HIPPOCRATES

I first learned about Dr. Nooshin and her novel work involving nature while browsing YouTube, searching for an interesting talk to watch while folding laundry. Being a nature enthusiast myself, I was on the lookout for anything that explored nature and helped me learn. When Dr. Nooshin's TED Talk, titled *Prescribing Nature for Health*, scrolled onto my screen, I gave it a click.

Nooshin Razani's TEDx Talk was the second I had seen that covered environmental psychology. The concept was once novel to me but has revealed its meaning to me through this book more clearly. Before I knew it had a scientific name, I simply referred to it as nature magic, the hidden wonders of how nature affects the mind. As it turns out, scientists had already come up with a name a bit more professional than the one I coined. Environmental psychology, what I used to call nature magic, is a relatively new branch of psychology. It is the study of how people interact and engage with their surroundings—in this case, the natural environment they are in.

After attending UC San Francisco's medical school and earning her master's in public health from the Harvard School of Public Health, Dr. Nooshin's career and life path seemed as if it would follow the set and "typical" doctor path. But although Dr. Nooshin *did* eventually practice medicine through a different lens, she set herself apart in the world of medical professionals. She was one of the first to combine nature and health and explore the power of nature as a free and easy access tool for healing. As a trained Nature Champion by the National Environmental Education Fund & the US Bureau of Fish and Wildlife and a mother of three nature whisperers, Dr. Nooshin used her personal and professional knowledge to make a powerful change in her community.

But while her fame arose from her unique experiences and the novel intersection between health and the natural world, she gives credit to her children. Since they lived in an urban environment, Nooshin Razani and her family were hard-pressed to find places where her children could explore, play, and simply be. However, her children demonstrated the power of nature from even the smallest trees or the tightest patches of grass.

As Dr. Nooshin realized how much of an impact nature had on her children, she sought it out more actively. While each child found their own "safe place" and comfort zone within the natural world, their peace, happiness, and flourishing childhood became more evident. She wondered if the same health she saw in her own children could help her patients from the UCSF Benioff Children's Hospital Oakland. So began her research.

Nooshin was genuinely curious about exploring the concept of nature as a healer and learned that the average American spends only **7 percent** of their life outdoors (**12 percent** if you include car time). Increasingly, much of "outdoor time" is not spent in nature either. As society becomes more technologically advanced, the time we spend in nature seems to decrease consistently. While spending time outside, even in urban settings, is drastically better for health than remaining indoors, Dr. Nooshin found there was something *specific* to spending time in nature.

Out of the many remarkable studies that demonstrate the power of nature, one particularly intriguing data point was that after only **fifteen to twenty minutes** of forest bathing (the Japanese practice of shinrin-yoku) or simply being in nature, both our attention span and cognitive abilities increase (more on shinrin-yoku in later chapters). And through her research and the data compiled by others, science began to shine a very clear light that nature *could*, in fact, be used to heal.

After finding scientific backing to what she had seen in her own children, Dr. Nooshin put the intersection of nature and public health into play. She redesigned her hospitals to feature beautiful local environments and partnered with nearby parks. She and her fellow doctors began prescribing nature outings to patients who struggled with stress and social isolation. And because many of the patients and families at Nooshin Razani's clinic were lower income or struggled with poverty, nature proved to be the *perfect* prescription. Not only could they easily find it in the form of local parks, but it was completely free and extremely effective.

In addition to the nature imagery and the prescriptions, once a month, her clinic took patients and their families—along with a doctor and a ranger—on a bus to the park for a picnic and community building experience. But more important than the changes that Dr. Nooshin and her clinic made were the changes that patients themselves experienced. As she measured her progress and recorded the results, that same power of nature she had first experienced with her own three children showed itself in full to her patients as well.

Dr. Nooshin's story is one of many examples of the miraculous power of nature. The following chapters will cover other aspects of nature's power—that its ability to heal is greatly overlooked but also a somewhat revolutionary idea.

Along with Nooshin Razani and the Center for Nature and Health, based at UCSF Benioff Children's Hospital Oakland, other studies have highlighted nature's specific healing power. Two obvious examples are hotel and hospital views. For hotels, rooms with balconies or ones that overlook beautiful natural scenery are in far more demand because of how much they positively affect our minds. Like how Dr. Nooshin redesigned her clinic, studies have shown that patients who get a natural view from their hospital beds recover *faster* than those who don't.

Nature is a vitally important aspect of our world for a variety of reasons. From the tangible to more spiritual benefits that it provides, nature serves as a backbone to society. The World Wildlife Fund, an organization dedicated to preserving and restoring the health of the natural world, expertly highlights why it is important to value nature:

> *The natural world is an incredible wonder that inspires us all. It underpins our economy, our society, indeed our very existence. Our forests, rivers, oceans, and soils provide us with the food we eat, the air we breathe, the water we irrigate our crops with. We also rely on them for numerous other goods and services we depend on for our health, happiness and prosperity.*

Within the next two chapters of Part 3: What I Call Nature Magic, we will learn more about how and why nature affects our minds and bodies, exploring a hidden and somewhat less popular side of the world of nature. But regardless of whether this side of nature is obvious, it is still vitally important for both our health and our understanding of the natural world.

Nooshin Razani's children followed their hearts as they explored nature by finding animals to look at or climbing trees. Because Dr. Nooshin watched and learned from them, she brought to light the extraordinary healing powers of nature.

CHAPTER 11

FOLLOW YOUR HEART... BUT TAKE YOUR BRAIN WITH YOU

———

RONNA SCHNEBERGER

What is a backbone to our world and an ever-evolving masterpiece of wonder? And also community builder, stress reducer, mood enhancer, and healer?

What has stark diversity of appearance and behavior but is undeniably unified by its beauty, strength, adaptability, and untouched power? And what has been part of human lives since the beginning of time and will still stand strong long after we are gone?

What creates sights that no man can recreate—sounds that no musician can compare—and smells, tastes, and feels that inspire more greatness than anything any human genius can produce? If you thought the answer was God, bonus points to you.

The answer I was looking for was Mother Nature.

The two biggest things that come to my mind whenever I hear the word *nature* are beauty and power. More than anything, those two words define the whole of the vast natural world. From pitch black nights illuminated by millions of shimmering stars, to mountain ranges that juxtapose their snowy peaks, to the lush and flourishing forests near their bases, to the Caribbean waters that shine a turquoise blue so bright that the sky seems to reflect its glow, the beauty of nature is undeniable.

While humans have certainly created beautiful pieces of architecture, art, and design, the mind is never as awed and inspired by downtown skyscrapers as it is by the peaks that seem to kiss the stars. As the beauty of nature is unrivaled in our world, so is its power.

The power of nature is unmatched even in our technologically advanced and developed world. From its obvious power through tsunamis, hurricanes, earthquakes, or volcanic eruptions, to the less visible (but more tangible) power that flows through the wild animals of forests and plains and through the mighty fish of the sea, the power of nature is big and great. But I would like to touch on another power of nature as well, a much less obvious one—the power to affect human minds.

Before we talk in depth about the psychological power of nature, I would like to back up a little bit. Before we continue learning about how and why nature affects our minds, consider the quote that has become the title of this chapter: Follow Your Heart…But Take Your Brain with You.

I first heard this quote from my father as he tried to help me with my chronic decision-making struggles. I was stuck in limbo between the choice I *thought* I should make and the choice that I actually *wanted* to make. While the poetry of the words resonated with me deeply, the truth of the quote was the tool that pried me away from indecision.

The quote above was from Austrian psychiatrist and psychotherapist Alfred Adler. The power behind Adler's words is that when making important or difficult decisions, people often assume they must follow either their heart *or* their brain. Some assume that the passionate or heart-felt choice is the best way to go in making decisions, and others rely on logic and reasoning. What Adler provides is a way to make a decision inspired by true and genuine passion but also grounded in a levelheadedness and common sense detached from biased emotion. He provides an invaluable both-and option.

From the moment I first heard the quote, I saw it as a best-of-both-worlds decision-making tool and a way to flow through life in a much more authentic and wise way. And while I first thought the biggest purpose of this quote was to assist with decision-making in people's love lives, I realized its power outside the world of romance. Its place was in the heart of environmental psychology.

I previously talked about Dr. Nooshin Razani, the revolutionary pediatrician who combined nature and public health in a novel way to help the patients in her clinic heal faster, cheaper, and more effectively. Dr. Nooshin was the *second* person I learned about who studied environmental psychology and put it into practice.

In this chapter, I would like to look at the woman who *first* introduced me to this concept—Ronna Schneberger.

Like Dr. Nooshin, Ronna's TEDx Talk on environmental psychology was one of the first times I saw research back up my own beliefs around the natural world. Ronna Schneberger was credible and poised throughout her TEDx Talk, but what stood out to me most, aside from it being incredibly engaging, was that she perfectly put Alfred Adler's instructions into practice.

Leading with her heart, inspired her to spend habitual and quality time in the beauty of the natural world. Letting her passions guide her actions, she began leading yoga classes in the heart of flawless natural environments, including others in the peaceful wonders of being in the outdoors.

But as Adler emphasized, Schneberger brought her brain with her into those natural environments. After several years of study, research, and dedication, she discovered that science and data backed up her love for nature.

Ronna Schneberger was the first to introduce me to the study of environmental psychology. She pulled my interest in the subject from a slight curiosity to a genuine and strong fascination through her inspiring words and her perfect application of "following your heart but taking your brain with you."

"Three years ago," Ronna started off her TED Talk, "I took out a client, and what happened that day completely transformed how I understood the power of nature."

Pausing for emphasis, she scanned the room before explaining to her audience that particular client's life experiences before recounting what had happened on that specific day in nature. Her client, Val, a twenty-year executive of a prominent oil and gas company, had recently laid off hundreds of people from the company. Even though she was extremely successful, because of the tension and stress that revolved around her duties and decisions, she could not seem to find the pause button on her life that would give her time to reflect and recharge. Reaching out, Val had asked Ronna to go out into nature with her to help Val regain the clarity she needed around her life. And Ronna, having a long-time experience of teaching yoga, meditation, and lifestyle coaching within the natural world, happily agreed.

"I remember this day very clearly," Ronna says, beginning her recounting of that day. "I took Val to a local lake, just down the valley here, and it was late September, so there was a little bit of snow on the top of the mountains. The air was crisp, and there was nobody on the trail."

Ronna switches the image on the screen to one of the lake where they had gone that day. The view was breathtaking, to say the least. The sky was a piercing blue and filled with wispy clouds that seemed to form halos around the peaks of the mountains. Even from the screen, the mountains radiated beauty. From the white and black tops of snow and rock, their colors shifted to a gray and then the green of trees and vegetation at the base. The steepness of the slopes suddenly dropped off into several cliffs of stone flowing into the lake. A slight wind created ripples and streaks of light on the surface of the water as it glowed the same deep blue found in the tail feathers of peacocks. And around the shallower shorelines, small trees and shrubs gave way to a gravelly gray beach.

Pausing Ronna's TEDx Talk as it played on my computer, I stared at that picture in silence. By just looking at the raw and pure nature of Alberta, Canada, I could feel myself becoming more relaxed and at peace.

Clicking to another picture, Ronna gave the audience a second taste of what she and her client experienced that day. This time, the picture overlooked a forest that seemed ablaze. Fiery leaves of orange and yellow brought the treetops to life and formed an artist's palette of colors throughout the forest greenery.

"The air was crisp, there was nobody on the trail, and the trees were beautiful that day," she continued. "It was just a perfect day to ponder life. And what I did was begin the day with sense meditation for my client to switch gears, and then I invited her to walk slowly through the forest. And as she came out of this dense, mature pine forest, she came into this scene. It was a fairly new burn in the last ten years. And as she came through that threshold, she just stopped. I was a little ways away, ahead of her, and I remember looking back and thinking, *Oh, Val's having one of those powerful nature moments.* I want to talk to you today about these powerful nature moments. You see, those who are nature-wise have an edge in today's busy and distracted world."

Because I was not watching this TED Talk live or in person, I paused the video again to digest what I had heard. Closing my eyes, I replayed Ronna's words over in my mind: *those who are nature-wise have an edge in today's busy and distracted world.*

Nature wisdom was not a concept I had ever thought about before, nor was the idea that *being* nature-wise could give a person an advantage in life. And interestingly enough, nature wisdom was not something that Ronna was initially familiar with either.

For seven years before her life-changing experience with Val, Ronna had led yoga-hiking retreats—a combination of walking meditation and eco-yoga in the heart of amazing natural locations—along with leading leadership walks that consisted of walking meditation and reflective questioning while outdoors. Although Ronna's yoga and hiking business was relatively small, one common theme throughout almost all the retreats and leadership walks was the participants' response to the experience. Not only did everybody love it, but many had profound insights while in nature or reported how necessary the experience had been for their lives.

At first, Ronna didn't think much of her clients' responses. To her, the positive psychological effects of spending time in nature were simply intuitive. While these comments and reports kept rolling in, Ronna began to realize something else was going on although she couldn't pinpoint it. The tipping point was on that nature hike with Val.

As the two women walked back after the meditative hike, Val began to gush about all the amazing insights she experienced that day. Ronna couldn't help but wonder how such a basic experience (simply being out in nature) could have such tremendously beneficial results. From then on, Ronna began to explore the scientific explanation for the seemingly psychological powers of nature. And eventually, after talking to one of her clients about her interest in how being in nature seemed to greatly affect the minds of individuals, she discovered shinrin-yoku, or forest bathing.

TAKING YOUR BRAIN WITH YOU

During the past several years, it has taken many research studies to understand more about how and why simply spending time in nature positively affects the human mind in profound ways.

Nature has the power to build community, reduce stress, and improve moods. Although recent research supports these claims, according to an article from *National Geographic*, "While Japan is credited with the term *shinrin-yoku*, the concept at the heart of the practice is not new. Many cultures have long recognized the importance of the natural world to human health."

In the chapter Nature and Nurture, I talked about nature prescriptions and the increase in their popularity. One specific nature prescription that has received a significant amount of credibility and has inspired much action around environmental psychology is *shinrin-yoku*, the Japanese practice of forest bathing.

Forest bathing, simply put, is actively spending time in forests. Some people like to bathe in Epsom salts to relieve their stress, but many people have begun to realize that bathing in the sights, smells, and sounds of the forest is one of the most effective stress-relievers in the world.

"Forest bathing is not just for the wilderness-lover; the practice can be as simple as walking in any natural environment and consciously connecting with what's around you."

—SUNNY FITZGERALD

The modern practice of forest bathing originated in Japan in the 1980s to provide relief and relaxation for its Japanese citizens. With a rise in technology, urbanization, and jobs that required high amounts of desk and computer work, Japan began to witness a decline in the health levels of those urban individuals. So with a two-fold goal of preserving the natural forests and environments in Japan and striving to restore the health of their citizens, *shinrin-yoku* emerged. And because of the remarkable benefits of *shinrin-yoku,* its popularity grew.

While many studies examined how nature affected the mind, two prominent studies highlighted excellent *physical* results from being in nature. These studies researched how being in nature affected the participating individuals' levels, activity, and other information around the natural killer cells (the cells known for killing virally infected cells and detecting and controlling early signs of cancer).

Within these studies, they found that not only did the NK (natural killer) activity increase by around **50 percent** compared to the control group, but also the presence of a variety of other important cells and proteins increased as well. One of those studies states, "These findings indicate that a forest bathing trip can increase NK activity, and that this effect at least partially mediated by increasing the number of NK cells and by the induction of intracellular anti-cancer proteins."

But that is not the only health benefit nature can achieve. Many studies around environmental psychology and how nature affects the human mind have been conducted. One study by the University of Derby and The Wildlife Trusts, where participants were asked to engage with nature every day for a month, had *very* positive outcomes.

"Intuitively, we knew that nature was good for us as humans, but the results were beyond brilliant," said Lucy McRobert, nature matters campaigns manager for The Wildlife Trusts.

"Looking at beauty in the world is the first step to purifying the mind."

—AMIT RAY

And looking from a more mental health side, nature can also perform wonders on the mind by lowering stress levels.

A blog post by Forest Holidays found that, compared to urban walks, forest bathing yields a **12.4 percent** decrease in the stress hormone cortisol. Not only did the levels of cortisol drop significantly, but they *stayed* low for several months afterward.

Professor Yoshifumi Miyazaki at Chiba University in Japan has been researching the benefits of forest bathing since 2004. He determined that *phytoncides*, a chemical released by trees to protect themselves from insects and predators, are the root cause of the drop in cortisol and the rise in NK activity. It is truly fascinating to know that the defensive chemicals released by forests affect our minds so positively that they can increase our natural killer cells and decrease our stress levels.

Talk about the power of nature!

But forests are not the only natural environments that perform wonders in the mind. Research has backed up that oceans—or simply being near, in, or on the water—can positively affect the mind too. As with the green of forests, the blue of the sky and the sea have a drastic calming effect on those present.

> "The ocean stirs the heart, inspires the imagination, and brings eternal joy to the soul."
>
> —WYLAND

In his book *Blue Mind*, marine biologist Wallace Nicholas explores the neuroscience of how people's brains react to being near the ocean. His book explores the healing power of water and studies whether the best way to protect the oceans and advocate for marine conservation is by helping people associate the positive feelings they experience when around the sea with actual environmental change.

In an interview with the *Washington Post*, Nicholas answered questions around the 'blue mind,' a term he coined, bringing more light to the power of this particular aspect of nature:

> *[The 'blue mind'] refers to a mildly meditative, relaxed state that we find ourselves in when we are in, on, or under water. It's something I've been experiencing and observing my whole life. As marine biologists, we don't get a chance to talk about that feeling seriously and publicly. Yet, it is the reason I became a marine biologist. At the same time, none of the books about water ever talked about the human brain.... When we step away from our high-stressed lives and step into nature, we get a shift. Physiologically, our brains and bodies change. We relax, and the quality of our thought changes.*

But while the wonderful mental effects of nature might be a new concept to some, many others have long accepted them. Marketing experts have always seemed to be one step ahead in understanding how humans' brains work, and environmental psychology is no exception. Because nature positively affects the brain, many companies have included aspects of nature within their commercials or general brands to help connect a positive emotion with their product. Here are some obvious examples:

Busch: In many, if not all, of Busch's commercials, lush forests and snowy mountains are used to create an identity attached to an aspect of nature.

Corona: Like Busch, Corona uses beach and ocean themes in most of its advertisements to appeal to its customers.

Ford: Unlike Busch and Corona, Ford commercials take place in a variety of environments, but prominent environments for their truck advertisements were desert or rocky terrains.

NOBULL: Even NOBULL, a recently founded CrossFit company, dedicated an entire apparel collection to a beautiful floral and gardening theme.

Returning to Alfred Adler's quote, following your heart but taking your brain with you is key to reaping the full benefits of taking time in nature. Sometimes, especially with our extreme hustle-culture, dedicating time simply to *be* in nature can seem unproductive or wasteful, but the benefits are invaluable compared to the time "wasted."

Sometimes I feel awkward setting aside a chunk of time to just sit and listen to the birds and the wind. Yet, by allowing myself to follow my heart into nature and taking my brain with me to reinforce its importance, I can experience the full and amazing powers of the natural world.

CHAPTER 12

THE POWER OF NATURE

—

"To stand at the edge of the sea, to sense the ebb and flow of the tides, to feel the breath of a mist moving over a great salt marsh... is to have knowledge of things that are as nearly eternal as any earthly life can be."

—RACHEL CARLSON

THE POWER OF NATURE

Rachel Carlson, in all her wisdom, was spot on. Like many aspects of nature, the ocean, the tide, the sand, and the seas contain an extraordinary power that inspires a wonder to all who behold it. We previously discussed the hidden but extraordinary powers nature can have on our minds and bodies. Through the stories and experiences of Nooshin Razani and Ronna Schneberger, the *what, why,* and *how* of this specific vein of environmental psychology has begun to solidify.

While researching the effects nature has on our minds, I connected with a lady named Shannon Stewart. My dad had met Shannon several months prior through their shared love and interest in education. Still, while my dad's passion is focused on uprooting traditional education, Shannon's interest followed a slightly different track. Through her love for nature, she had developed a desire to include raw nature into school schedules. When I say "raw" nature, I am simply referring to the presence of nature *other* than the grass or trees surrounding the school. For Shannon, that "raw" nature took the form of gardens.

Shannon understood the importance of spending time in nature. She made a name for herself in the education realm by developing a thriving and successful garden as part of a local school. And through this overlap of nature, I had the opportunity to connect with and eventually interview her.

Shannon Stewart grew up in Austin, Texas, a city not far from Houston (where I live) and one with which I am very familiar. Through numerous swim competitions held in or around Austin, it has become clear that, more so than Houston, Austin prioritizes outdoor activities and events. With the Colorado River flowing right along the edge of downtown and various restaurants and stores, bikers, runners, and the crazy people who ride the motorized scooters at thirty miles per hour on the narrow city sidewalks are common sights throughout the whole of Austin, Texas.

And along with the rest of the city, Shannon grew up outdoors as well. She enjoyed spending time outside so much because of the simplicity and freedom of the experience.

From climbing trees, to playing in streams, to being chased by water moccasins, Shannon spent little of her free time within the confines of her room or house. When she moved to Southern California, her life followed functionally the same path.

And just as her youth flowed around nature, exploration, and the outdoors, her college and career began with the same trajectory. From marine biology internships right after college, to animal training at Six Flags and later at Sea World, to her current garden project, the importance of animals, nature, and spending time outdoors proved a critical and dominant theme throughout her life.

"I just turned forty-five last week," Shannon told me during our interview, "and honestly, I can't remember [being in] a job that didn't involve me being outdoors. And I can't even fathom having a job or being in a career that forces me to be inside all the time."

Shannon's various interning and training experiences helped her develop a greater knowledge of the power of nature and a greater understanding of different aspects of it. But she only witnessed the power of nature as a teacher during her gardening class, the Sage Garden Project. Throughout her childhood, nature had taught her resiliency, problem-solving, and adaptability. As she got deeper within her garden class, she began to see how powerfully nature affected her students as well.

Here is a snippet of conversation as Shannon and I discuss the power of nature within her garden and elsewhere:

Shannon Stewart: *I walk [outside] every time I experience frustration, sadness. I get outside and walk. There's something about just that motion and walking past trees and seeing trees and living things that shifts your mindset. It kind of gets you out of this permanency feeling that you feel like you'll always feel like this and nothing will change because I feel like that's where those suicidal thoughts come in for many people. And it's that fine line between really understanding that this is not permanent and that you don't have to feel this way forever and actually taking that next step to end your life. And outdoors and nature, and just being in touch with those things, and breathing fresh air, not staring at a screen anymore, those things really, really, really contribute to someone's mental shift in a good way.*

Olivia Barnes: *Hmm, yeah. Very, very true. And how have you pulled that, what you were just talking about, into your gardening class?*

Shannon Stewart: *Yeah, so it's kind of like a weaving effect. It's not just like, Hey guys, here's a seed. I'm going to show you how to grow it. We have this garden space. We're going to work with the animals that want to come into our gardens. We're going to have friends; we're going to have foes.*

And going back to resiliency, being outside is a good thing. It's trial-and-error thinking. It sets kids up for real life, like, things aren't perfect, and things can get in the way. The cabbage moth is going to devour your broccoli plant. Okay, what are we going to do next time to prevent that? How can we harvest this plant so that it will continue to come back for us? And don't take the whole head [of lettuce] off; we want to leave some for other people. It's this whole "bigger than you" thought, "bigger than you" thinking. And there's just so much that can be taught from the gardens.

Olivia Barnes: *Yeah, and I completely agree. An interesting personal story about gardens, I recently lost a friend to a very traumatic accident. I was struggling emotionally during that time. But interestingly enough, my dad was out of town that same week, and it was my job to water the garden. And just being in the garden for fifteen minutes daily and experiencing the beautiful life and death cycles that come naturally within nature really helped me through that experience.*

[Content Removed]

Olivia Barnes: *Alright, so this is my last question for today, and this one is a little bit abstract, so I am completely okay if you do not have an answer. If there's one word you could use to describe your relationship with nature, what would it be and why?*

Shannon Stewart: *I would say it would be either change or dynamic. We talked about this before that there's one constant thing in life: there will always be change. There's one constant thing with things happening in nature: change. But dynamic, I just feel like there's just so much power and wisdom that comes from nature, too. We can get so much from it. I don't feel like* *we've given enough to it that it can give back to us. And that's where I believe that it's just this dynamic entity that just gives us life.*

Shannon Stewart's life and experiences around nature, specifically education and nature, are inspirational, to say the least. Through various stories (a few too personal to include in this book), Shannon has shown how influential nature can truly be.

Nature is so amazing because it can be molded to suit people differently. For instance, while my older brother and younger sister both find peace within the snow-capped Rocky Mountains and my godparents enjoy the dry terrain of New Mexico, my greatest love of nature lies within the ocean.

Many experiences have taught me how to adapt and become more resilient toward the unpredictability and the constant changes of the natural world. The following story demonstrates the more dynamic (as Shannon Stewart put it) side of Mother Nature.

It was a typical day at Galveston Beach. A lonely sky with nothing but the scorching sun to keep it company stretched into the distance until it dipped below the watery horizon. Seagulls, attracted by the commercialized beachfront restaurants, screeched and called to one another as they peppered the sky searching for snacky treats. The waves rolled in and out upon the scratchy brown sand with a monotony so soothing it almost sounded as if the whole ocean itself was whispering.

But through all of this poetry, this fact remains: the beaches of Galveston Island are far from beautiful.

With numerous developed stores and restaurants, highways that border the sandy and rocky shores, tanks and cargo ships dotting the horizon, the never-ending smell of oil and rotting seaweed, and the brownish, muddy water, it was hard to imagine Galveston as a natural environment.

Regardless of how obstructed and trashed this piece of nature was, without fail, I have always found peace in its rocking waves.

It was a typical day at Galveston Beach, as noisy as ever and hotter than ever as my family and I parked our car by the sea-wall. We grabbed our towels, boards, chairs, and tent, trying to make it down to the sand in one trip. A misty breeze rolled in from the sea as we made our way to a spot of unoccupied sand and set our belongings down. It didn't take long to set up our tent and chairs, and in no time, my siblings and I were racing across the beach as the burning sand changed to wet sand and then to water. Laughing, we ran full speed into the waves until they got too big, the bottom became too far away, and we were forced to swim.

We spent most of the morning in the ocean, lying on our backs and letting the rhythm of the sea lull us into a stupor or riding the waves back toward shore. And after lunch, our parents accompanied us to the wide stretch of sea. We would take turns on the boards or challenge each other to swim races into the waves or simply bob up and down, matching the swells.

As my brother, sister, and dad raced back to shore, either on the boards or on their stomachs, my mother and I relaxed on the rolling waves, gazing out into the vast sky and endless ocean while waiting for their return. We both held onto a board, using its buoyancy to keep our bodies afloat. Our feet dangled beneath us, searching for the floor far below. I tilted my head back and closed my eyes, listening to the rushing waves, the gulls, and the urbanized noises of civilization, and letting the sun bathe my face in warmth.

After a while, my mother spoke, "You ok, Lu?"

I smiled, opening my eyes, and looked at her.

"Yeah, I just…I mean…," I struggled for the right words to express how I felt. "It's just so nice out here."

My mom smirked, gazing at the defiled nature of Galveston Beach. I followed her eyes, looking at the trash and the ships and the cloudy water, and sighed.

"Ok, well maybe it's not the nicest of beaches," I said, "but it's still the ocean, and I mean…."

I shrugged as I, again, struggled to find the words.

My mom looked at me and said, "You always have loved the ocean, haven't you." Her eyes crinkled at their edges as she smiled. "You have always been able to see the beauty of nature that others just overlook."

We sat quietly for a while, letting the waves move us up and down. Then she spoke again.

"Still, I'd be surprised if there's still anything alive in Galveston Bay. I mean, like, I'd half expect to see a three-eyed fish or something here."

We laughed as she made a face, imitating a fish mutated by the trash and chemicals in the water. With three-eyed fish still on my mind, I gazed out at the horizon, letting its vastness and mystery wash over me and calm me from the inside out.

Suddenly, I gasped.

"What?" my mom asked.

My heart racing, I said, "I saw a dorsal fin...over there." I pointed to where I had seen it.

My mom's casual expression changed in a heartbeat to one of fear.

"Are you sure?"

But no sooner had she finished her question when it appeared again: a dorsal fin, sleek and gray, that appeared for a second and then vanished beneath the waves.

Without hesitation, my mom said, "Oh, I'm getting outta here. I'm not going to get eaten by a shark today."

Panic rising in my mind, I began following my mom. I had hardly taken two strokes when I glanced back again. The dorsal fin was hardly a couple of meters away, and this time, as I watched it, I saw something I hadn't noticed before.

"Mom!" I called out, "I don't think it is a shark! Sharks don't swim like that, and I saw a blow."

"I don't know," my mom said. Unconvinced, she continued to swim toward the shore.

I watched her swim away, slightly annoyed that she was willing to let me get eaten by the shark but slightly grateful that she had not commanded me to get out of the water. After she took a couple of strokes more, I turned back around to where I had seen the fin.

Suddenly, my initial panic was gone, replaced by...excitement? Anticipation? I didn't know, but I began to swim, hard, toward where I last saw the fin, and then suddenly, maybe eight feet away, I saw a dolphin. Two or three other dorsal fins also broke the surface as a pod of dolphins swam right before my fingertips.

Although my life and the life of those cloudy charcoal-gray dolphins overlapped only for a second, it was one of the most defining moments in my life. In that brief moment, it was as if I became part of something bigger and so much more beautiful than I could ever imagine. But not only was I a part of this bigger something, but I also belonged there as well. I was terrified to the point of reverence for those dolphins. As their dorsal fins slipped below the surface and they vanished beneath the waves, I began to cry.

It was a disgusting cry too: tears streamed down my face and my nose ran as my mouth hung completely open. They were deep sobs, genuine and spontaneous. They tugged at my heart in a way I didn't know was possible as they rang out in the open air. As I watched the waves where the dolphins had just disappeared, I felt renewed and alive. It was like the kind of feeling I get when adrenaline kicks in, but stronger somehow, and purer.

A significant amount of adrenaline was definitely coursing through my veins after I saw those dolphins, but I did not become restless, twitchy, or agitated. Instead, a sense of peace and calm came over me, along with a sense of recognition and a clear understanding of how small I was in the vast and extraordinary natural world. It was a beautiful feeling, and I wanted it to last forever.

For those of you who read the Introduction to this book, this is the same story, the same life-changing encounter I had with those dolphins on that typical day at Galveston Beach. And as I look back on that day when I saw my first wild dolphin, I now know that my tears originated from a place of true and genuine awe. I had never experienced awe like that before, and I have not experienced it since, but I know that experience is one that I will never forget.

Nooshin Razani quoted in her TEDx Talk that psychologists break down awe as the combination of fear, happiness, and pleasure, all together, and I completely agree. Like Rachel Carlson said, the awe that I experienced from that moment with the dolphins gave me knowledge of things as wondrous and eternal as any earthly thing can be.

RECAP

PART 3 - WHAT I CALL NATURE MAGIC SUMMARY:

Over the last three chapters, I have been exploring nature magic (a.k.a. environmental psychology) and how nature positively affects the mind. And because of the research, stories, and experiences seen, read, and heard about, I have developed a newfound understanding of the hidden wonders of the natural world.

While my research answered almost all my questions, a big one remains. Earlier in this book, we looked behind the minds of elite athletes, searching to understand the mental aspect of what makes them so elite. So, if nature worked so well on the minds of regular individuals, what do *athletes'* minds look like while in nature, and how does nature affect *them*?

PART IV

RETURNING TO THE MINDS OF ATHLETES

CHAPTER 13

SAME BUT DIFFERENT

A WATERY JUXTAPOSITION

My hands clutched the blocks. Their metal frame was cold and wet against my fingers as the textured plastic of the board dug into my hands. I pounded my foot against the wedge, confirming its stability, and looked into the water beneath me.

I could barely see myself on the surface of the water as my reflection swayed back and forth, matching the ripples and disturbances. I closed my eyes briefly and muttered a prayer for peace, humility, and courage.

And then, from the staticky speaker at the edge of the pool, the official called, "Take your mark."

My eyes flew open as every muscle in my body prepared to activate. I focused all my attention on the gun, leaning onto my toes, anticipating the call...then ...*CRACK!* I launched myself from the block, throwing myself into the air as if I had wings, forming my body into a tight streamline.

The water was cold when I entered, and the combined adrenaline rush from excitement and the shock from the icy water set me on fire. Speed was my partner-in-crime when it came to swimming the 50 free. As I broke through the surface, racing toward a victory, it was all I thought about.

In my periphery, I could see the girls in the lanes beside mine. Their shadowy figures matched my own as we battled each other, desperate to gain a lead.

Only four and a half seconds had passed by the time I had reached the cross-stripe of small tiles that marked half a 25. The black line that ran down the middle of the lane loomed daunting and bold (and slightly reflective) as I swam above it. *Big kick*, I told myself. *Big kick, big arms, deep catch, quick tempo, quick breath, good body position.* My mind whirred with information as I sped toward the wall, focusing on form and determined to swim as fast as I was able.

Nine seconds had passed now as I flew underneath the flags, approaching the wall—9.5 seconds, then 10 seconds, then 10.5, and then 11 as I flipped, channeling my speed through the turn. My legs were cannons, cocked and ready to fire as my feet touched the wall: 11.38 seconds.

I glided off the wall, feeling the water stream by my body. Rotating from my side onto my stomach, I kicked to the surface. I could see my teammate in the lane next to mine. Her underwaters were so much better than mine. As I swam on the surface, she kept up with me easily, utilizing her graceful and powerful dolphin kick.

I let out a stream of bubbles that tickled my face as they rose and contemplated the speed and ease that my teammate possessed while swimming underwater. I watched her again as she kicked to the surface, noting her body position, the origin of her kick, and her unbelievable propulsion.

I sighed again, letting out another ticklish stream, and turned my attention back to my own swimming. My stroke had a lot of room for improvement. I took my mind off autopilot and focused on my awareness of the water, feeling the pressure on my forearms as I pulled, managing my head and chest position as I breathed, sensing the water around my feet as I kicked. I let my hips ride up to the surface and tried my best to work with the water, using its motion to my advantage instead of fighting against it. I visualized swimming downhill, using the momentum to carry me along.

Approaching my turn, I thought again about my teammate and her incredible dolphin kick. As I flipped and pushed off the wall, I tried my best to imitate her form, using my core and kicking from my chest down, not just with my legs. It *felt* faster, but who knows if it actually was.

I finished my 200 warmup and stood at the shallow end as my lane-mates finished behind me. Seeing me standing idle, one of my coaches came over to talk.

"How'd you feel in the water today?" she asked.

"Pretty good. I've been trying to work on my catch and stuff because the last meet didn't go as well as I would have hoped."

She nodded thoughtfully.

"Yeah, well, if you want to develop more distance-per-stroke, you are going to have to work on it in practice. That goes for your kick as well. It's gonna hurt a lot in practice, but then you will be much more prepared for meets."

Then she smiled, "It's like what Brené Brown says, right? 'Embrace the suck.'"

I smiled back. I was not a huge fan of "embracing the suck" in practice, but my coach was right if I worked on form and technique in practice (even when it sucked), having good form in a race would be *that* much easier.

I continued, "It's also like what Coach always says, about being smart in practice and being dumb in a meet, like working on technique and endurance in practice so that when it's race time, you don't have to think about anything." I laughed as I thought about my own racing experience. "The problem is that I usually do the opposite. I overthink races and under-think practice. I'm gonna have to work on that."

We finished our conversation, and as the rest of my teammates finished their 200, my coach assigned the first main set of the day. By the time she finished explaining it, most of my team was grimacing. I, however, smiled. This set was going to hurt bad, and I knew it, but I also knew that it would make me a better swimmer, and *that* was exciting.

"Alright! You guys understand the set?" my coach asked. We nodded in reply. "Great, then y'all can leave at the top."

The clock read forty-five seconds, fifteen away from when our set would begin. I sighed, mentally preparing myself for the upcoming set. I visualized the pain that I would feel; I acknowledged the discomfort and mental stress that I would endure and did my best to convince my mind that I could do it even though the set would hurt.

But the mind is a complicated thing. And as I have learned throughout my swimming career, it can have an incredibly negative influence on a person's performance even if that person is completely physically capable. I sighed again as the clock read fifty-seven seconds…fifty-eight…fifty-nine. Then I inhaled deeply. I sank underwater, formed my streamline, and pushed off the wall.

My feet wiggled out of the water as my hands touched the bottom of the pool. I scrunched my nose to my face and let out a slow stream of bubbles, trying to keep the water out as I hung suspended upside down.

Doing handstands was always so much easier in water than on land. As my sister and I pretended to be gymnasts, doing weightless flips and acrobatics in the water, I was grateful for the chance to experience leisurely swimming. Being a competitive swimmer, I rarely had the opportunity to just *play* in the water.

After a few moments of doing a handstand, I arched my back and came to the surface. My sister emerged beside me, sputtering and furiously wiping her face to get the water out of her eyes.

"Ughhh," she moaned, "I god wader ind my nose." She squeezed her nose, making it turn red as her voice became warped in the process.

I looked at my sister and laughed. She scowled at me in response, annoyed that I found her pain humorous, and tried to drag me underwater to no avail. After several minutes of laughing, splashing, and fruitless struggling, she gave up.

My sister, an ex-competitive swimmer but still an incredible athlete, pushed away from me, rolling onto her back and staring into the blue sky dotted with puffy balls of fluff. Even though she hadn't trained or competed in several years, her grace in the water is forever impressive.

Being the obnoxious sister that I am, I sank underwater, pushing off the bottom with stealth and glided along until I was directly underneath Ellie, preparing to scare her. The sun was above us, and as I stared at her silhouette, I lost all desire to disturb the peace. I lay on my back on the bottom of the pool and watched her as gentle ripples moved her body ever so slightly. Utilizing my ability to hold my breath, I closed my eyes and simply lay at the bottom of the pool. A couple of bubbles escaped my lips.

Suddenly I felt a heavy pressure on my stomach. As it pushed hard against me, I gasped, inhaling a lung-full of water, and pushed to the surface, sputtering and coughing. My sister heaved with laughter as I wracked my lungs for air.

Instant karma, I thought, annoyed.

As it turned out, my sister, who had been on the surface of the water above me, had wondered where I was. But as she tried to put her foot down on the bottom of the pool to stand up and look for me, her feet found me first. Ellie had stepped on me.

After listening to Ellie's reenactment of the story, I couldn't help but laugh alongside with her. Her storytelling was flawless. But as our laughter died, a silence fell around us. After a moment, she looked back up at the sky.

"The sky is beautiful today," she said. "It looks like the water feels, quiet."

She rolled back onto her back and floated effortlessly, absorbing the beauty. I followed suit and became lost in the mystery of the water and the poetry of the sky.

A wave rolled underneath me as I lay on my back and stared into the sky. It was a gray, cloudy day, the kind that tastes of adventure and danger and mystery all together. The waves were relatively big today, but the swells didn't crest until they were almost upon the shore, so I was able to lie peacefully, almost undisturbed by the splash-less waves that raced beneath me.

I breathed in deeply, then out and turned over. I was far away from the shore. My family still lay asleep in their matching green tents as I paddled back toward the beach. As the waves began to cap and crash down around me, swallowing water became habitual. The salty water left my tongue parched and my lips dry, but it tasted of a freedom I didn't want to let go.

It was my first time swimming in the ocean without the ground close by, and it was far more like racing than I had initially imagined. I experienced an ever-present level of fear and vulnerability both in the competition pool and in the open water, along with the thrill of courage and excitement of the unknown. And though the waves of nature might be bigger than any I might create in a pool and the respective floors might feel different beneath one's feet, I could still feel a connection between those overlapping worlds.

As I neared the shore, my feet brushed the bottom and I paused, floating horizontally and gazing at the waking sky. Light shone through cracks in the clouds like rivers of gold as the sun began its ascent. A faint orange tinged the dark sea, giving it the appearance of smoldering charcoals. I could feel the warmth of the morning rays as my face floated along the active sea surface.

But as many similarities as I found between competitive swimming and swimming in the ocean, I could find that many differences too. The biggest is that while training and competing, my mind focused on myself (my form, technique, endurance, or speed). Still, when swimming in the open ocean, the vastness and beauty of it all drew my attention away from myself and toward the endlessness of the nature in which I was present.

The waves, with gentle nudges, pushed me toward the shore. Once the water was shallow enough to stand in, I picked myself up, walking through the water as it lapped at my ankles like a dog begging to play. As my feet crossed to dry sand, I turned back and stared at the sea, wider, deeper, more beautiful than any man-made pool. The science behind the way the ocean affects my mind has long been a mystery, but it is not so hard to understand why its elegance and danger inspire awe in me without fail. I am a swimmer, through and through. Whenever there is a pool or body of water, I'll be in it, feeling the waves, testing the waters, and finding my speed. But as committed as I am to the competition pool, the ocean will always be a home for me as well.

ATHLETES IN NATURE

At the end of The Power of Nature, I asked, How does nature affect the mind of athletes? Throughout this chapter and the rest of this book, I would like to explore that question in greater detail. And while I previously explored nature and how it affects us as humans, now I would like to narrow in on athletes specifically.

My interest in the relationship between, and the overlap of, sports and nature first began during the pandemic.

When the quarantine first began, the college kicked my team out of the campus natatorium that previously was our home base. And because the entire world basically shut down at the same time, we struggled to find alternative spaces to swim. Eventually, though, we settled down to train in a lake in the backyard of one of my teammates' houses until the world opened up again.

As green and murky as that lake might have been, my memories of training there will probably always be some of the most enjoyable of my swimming career. From the drastic change in scenery, to the countless memory-building experiences, and to witnessing the randomness of Texas weather, the lake was the favorite training location of many of my teammates, including me. But while I thoroughly enjoyed training at the lake, as the city began to recover from the initial blow of the pandemic and things began to open back up, we began swimming in pools closer to central Houston once more. With no more lake practice, the habitual time I had spent outside slowly began to shrink. I had never disliked swimming in indoor training facilities prior to COVID, but after training at the lake, I began to crave outdoor practice.

Although it has been almost eighteen months since the adventures at the lake, I have trained outdoors since then. I currently swim at an outdoor pool bordering a small grassy field surrounded by numerous trees and birds. So because of that pool location, spending time outdoors has again become a regular part of my life. But ever since the lake, I have started to wonder about the overlap of sports and nature. Training outdoors has been a huge blessing in allowing me to experience beautiful aspects of nature, like the moon, the serenade of birds, or the sunset. Although I train outside and there are numerous similarities to open water and natatorium swimming, the importance of setting aside time to be in nature is still critical.

But what about athletes who train indoors or athletes who cannot *directly* translate their sport to a nature-esque activity as I could with swimming? How do they find time in nature, and how do they interact with it?

As an athlete, nature's impact on my life is obvious. Just by reading the watery juxtaposition above, between competitive and open water swimming, I am clearly seriously passionate about being in the water. But although I can easily connect my sport to nature, most sports cannot directly translate into a nature-present activity as easily as swimming. For instance, let's compare track and field, specifically the track aspect of that sport, to baseball. While the act of running is different in a forest, on a beach, or on a track, it carries the same general principles and movements with it wherever it goes. Same with swimming. Baseball, however, would be difficult to stick easily in the natural world. *Maybe* you could find an open field or valley and hit around oranges or rocks with a large stick to reconstruct that sport in Mother Nature, but that would be a bit of a stretch. However, even if baseball cannot directly translate into an outdoor activity, almost all baseball stadiums are outdoors. By simply being outside, baseball players can benefit from the powers of nature.

It would fascinate me to research how training results differentiate based on the indoor or outdoor environment, but my focus has shifted away from the sport itself to the athlete instead. Based on my research, it would not surprise me if the ability to push through challenging training sessions greatly increased when outside. Because that specific overlap is not one of the primary veins of this book, I can only assume. I do know, however, that *all* the elite athletes I have spoken to, read about, and learned from who prioritize nature in their lives did not do so because they had a direct correlation between the sport they played and the aspect of nature in which they enjoyed spending time. They simply chose an environment that they enjoyed and made it a habit to spend time in it.

Nature is a vital part of our human existence, and I've realized it is a vital part of our athletic existence as well. It teaches resiliency, adaptability, and courage, all skills needed to survive and thrive as an athlete. By looking at the similarities between the four different types of swimming in which I participate, I have begun to realize that nature possesses a power specific to athletes, a power to shift the mindset from internal to external, a power to foster greater awareness, and a power to construct incomparable mental strength in the process.

RECAP

KEY TAKEAWAYS:

- Every athlete must prioritize spending time in nature, regardless of their **sport**.
- The power nature has on the **mind** can help athletes as well.

CHAPTER 14

THE BEAUTY OF THE CLIMB

THE BEAUTY OF THE CLIMB

Our world is fast-paced. It is powered by a hustle-culture engrained into our very way of life. It emphasizes that more is more and that busy work equals productivity. But what if *less* was truly more? What if living life slower yielded greater results?

The title of Ronna Schnegberger's TEDx Talk highlighted that people who are nature wise—those who understand nature's powers and spend intentional and quality time in it to strengthen, maintain, and restore their mental health—have an edge in today's society. And it is true. But nature does not only give Ronna's business clients an edge. The practice of spending time in nature, meditating, and escaping the bustle of our hustle-culture society has the power to give an edge to athletes as well.

"Don't run through life so fast. If you do, you'll miss the beauty and the wonder of the journey."

—MATT BARNES, CO-FOUNDER OF THE EDUCATION GAME (ALSO MY DAD)

Sometimes the life of an athlete can feel like a never-ending uphill climb. And in our technology-driven and rapid-moving society, the constant need to train, compete, and move to become a better athlete can become seriously overwhelming. But sometimes, to make the climb easier, we can pay attention to the little beautiful things along the trail—slow down and appreciate the journey.

Figuratively speaking, the beauties of the athletic climb are the birds and flowers that appear along the edge of the path. They give the hard work color and meaning. They are simple victories and private successes that line the path of an athlete's life. But birds and flowers are not only alive in the figurative world. Spending time in and paying attention to the aspects of nature that surround life can also have miraculous effects. And while this climb represents the difficult journey athletes take to become great, it can also mean a literal climb.

As I searched for athletes to interview about their relationship with their sport and with nature, I decided to reach out to a dear friend and the greatest athlete I know, Isabella Wakeham. Being a nationally competitive ninja, Isabella had been invited to compete on *American Ninja Warrior*, along with several other teens, against the pros. And even though she was only seventeen at the time of our interview, I knew she would give the pros a run for their money.

Our conversation circled around her experiences on the show, and I was reminded of how difficult Isabella's ninja career had been for her. She also reminded me that, through the stories below, crafted from individual research, our interview, and my own touches of creativity, whether it was literal climbing within ninja competition or climbing on boulders in Colorado with her family, gratitude for *every* aspect of the journey was essential to truly enjoying the climb.

The first obstacle required strength and patience to complete. It consisted of two long boards, attached by cords and poles to the ceiling above, with hollow indentions peppering the surfaces exposed to the area beneath. Two pegs sat at the beginning of the first board, hanging from thin passageways between the holes. Each peg had a round frame at the top and a T-shaped handhold at the bottom. One made progress by sliding the pegs into the holes (which were bigger than the round frame at the top of the pegs), removing them, and then inserting the peg into a hole and passageway farther down the board. But this progress could only be made with the athlete's feet off the floor. A mat lay several feet below the obstacle, waiting to catch whoever fell.

The countdown rang out–*beep...beep...beep...ding*! Three low notes and a high one marked the start of her clock as she began her course. Concentrating, she shifted her balance off the elevated starting platform and onto the first obstacle.

No words other than strength and grace could define her control as she began. Gripping the pegs, she lifted herself free from the platform, using her back, forearms, and shoulders to maintain her grip and work her way across the course.

"C'mon, Bells!" her teammates cheered, urging her on. "You got it!"

Keeping her eyes on the obstacle above her, she controlled her breathing, using precision to move the pegs above her head into holes farther down the obstacle. Her legs swung with her as she moved methodically, sliding and then lifting, then sliding the pegs again until she crossed the first board.

With a bit of a stretch, she continued onto the next board, using the support of her family, friends, teammates, and coaches below her to concentrate her energy on advancing to the next obstacle. In less than a minute, she was done. She grabbed a polished ring that hung in front of her and marked the second obstacle as another *Ding!* sounded in the gym, announcing the official completion of the first obstacle.

She completed the second obstacle much quicker than the first. Following its ladder-like structure, she quickly climbed down and then up its frame, mounting onto the third obstacle and completing it with speed. Four dings sounded as she finished the second, third, fourth, and fifth, using grip strength, balance, and stability to speed across the ninja run.

But her speed through her last four obstacles came to a pause as she approached the sixth. Chalking up her hands to ensure a good grip. She looked up at it, analyzing the technique she would need, the strength she would have to muster, and the concentration that would get her across without falling to the mat below.

She breathed in heavily, through her nose and out through her mouth. Clapping her hands together to knock off excess chalk, relieve stress, and loosen up her arms for the next run, she stepped up to the obstacle, preparing to jump. Her arms began to feel heavy, and she knew that as the run went on, she would have to start battling her mind, compelling her body to push to the finish even if the mind became overwhelmed with pain or fatigue.

Another breath. "You got this, Bella!" her coach called from beneath her.

Then she jumped, grabbing the bar above her. Using her legs and feet like a pendulum, she began swinging her body, maintaining control and keeping her eyes on the device she would have to grab midair as she swung from her current bar. Picking up speed, she gained momentum until her legs became parallel with the ground at the height of each swing.

"Launch Belle, launch it!"

And then she did. Using the momentum her legs had generated, she launched herself, letting go of the bar and flying through the air. Catching herself on the next aspect of the obstacle, she used her strength to slow the fall of her legs as she landed her grip.

Cheers rang up from the people around her, but concentration kept her from enjoying the praise in the moment. The obstacle was not over yet.

Monkey-barring her way across the rest of the obstacle, she put both hands on the bar, preparing once more for a swing. But this time, she would not have time to shake out her arms or take a breath before starting her next obstacle. The dismount from the sixth would be a swinging jump into the seventh.

Preparing for another swing by using the weight of her legs to act as a pendulum, she glanced at the next obstacle. It was daunting: imbalanced boards hung from the ceiling, forming a mismatched bridge to the next dismount. Trapezium-shaped boards formed the seventh obstacle, and they didn't hang parallel to the floor. She would have to be controlled in her landing and progression across this obstacle, and it would require severe grip strength and intense maintenance of stability to complete. Nervousness flickered momentarily in her mind.

Launching herself from the sixth obstacle, she landed on the seventh, a resounding *Ding!* confirming her success. Cheers erupted around her. The board rocked from her carried-over momentum as she scooched herself to the end of the first board. She swung again, catching the second board amidst even louder cheers, and proceeded onto the last board in that obstacle. Her arms felt heavy as she moved along the third board, and her muscles strained to support her hanging body weight as she prepared for the dismount.

Ding! Another successful obstacle completed. But the pain was setting in heavily. Her breathing was coming in heaves, and her arms ached. Chalking up her hands again, she looked at the next obstacle. Grip strength, patience, and overall intensity were needed to complete this obstacle. It was daunting, not to mention that it was her eighth obstacle of the run, and as she shook out her arms and heaved her chest for air, a wave of support swept over her.

"You got this, Bella!" someone said. "Once you start, don't stop. Just keep going."

Motivated by the encouragement (and by the clock), she stepped up to the obstacle. Placing one hand onto the first ledge and the other on a ledge farther away, she lifted herself off the platform. With one hand and then the other, she moved along the ledge until she got to a gap in the boards. The gap was not big, but it would be a stretch and would require concentration to hold.

Reaching out, Isabella grabbed onto the ledge of the second board. For a moment, she was suspended, arms wide, struggling to keep her grip. Her fingers strained as they tried to keep their tension on both ledges. But then, slipping off the obstacle, she lost her hold and fell to the mat beneath. As she landed on her feet in a crouch, a cry arose from the crowd around her.

Isabella Wakeham stood up and looked around. The breeze sang through the leaves of the trees and whistled across the rocky terrain around her. The loose strands of her hair whipped across her face as a gust of wind blew by her, rippling her hoodie and kicking up clouds of dirt on the dusty path.

The sun shone above her, but the intensity of its rays was dimmed by fluffy clouds that battled one another across the sky. From where she stood, she could see almost the entire valley. From rocky cliff faces to gurgling streams to towering greenery, nature called out and serenaded her ears, singing with freedom and beauty.

She followed her brothers and continued on the forest path, leaving boot prints in the dirt behind her. Absorbing the beauty of nature was a peaceful experience, yet she and her brothers still managed to stay rowdy and active as they threw sticks and rocks across shallow river beds, chased each other around bends and through the sparse trees, and shouted to the sky—letting their echoes drift across the vast expanse of nature.

As she reached a curve in the trail, a collection of boulders met her view. They varied in size, but they all demonstrated a calling of adventure. Along with their size, their shapes held variety, ranging from spherical rocks barely taller than she was to tall rectangular boulders that seemed to kiss the sky with their smoothed edges and shallow indentions. But through all the diversity, their color remained the same, a golden, reddish-brown that seemed to shine with warmth from the sky above. The boulders formed an intricate and artistic design as they wove through the mountainside and were peppered with trees and small shrubbery.

Racing her brothers to the nearest one, she began to climb, using her muscle memory from her training to find small indentions and protrusions to serve as hand and foot holds. The bronze surface of the boulder was warm and almost seemed to glow as the sun peeped through the clouds, gazing down at the three people scaling the rocks.

Reaching a resting point, she stopped and stood up. With a touch of pride, she looked at how far she had climbed: it hadn't been a small bolder by any stretch, and she had bounded up it quickly.

Like a mountain goat, she thought to herself, smiling.

Climbing was like second nature to her, but even still, she was amazed by the ease with which she gained height. Time seemed to pass in a blur as she slipped into a flow, climbing until she seemed to stand on top of the world. And though many of the movements that she made out in nature were the same as those in the gym, the burden of pushing her body's limits was gone. Her older brother had continued to a different boulder. So she followed him, calling out to her younger brother to keep up and jumping across gaps and cracks until the three siblings were reunited. And the view became even better.

They could see the dusty path down below, winding through the brush until it vanished from sight around the side of another rocky face. The rest of her family looked like figurines as they began climbing too, following in the footsteps of the more adventurous side of the family.

Walking up to the edge of the boulder on which she stood, she sat down, dangling her feet and letting the wind gently brush them around. Setting her hands behind her, she leaned back, letting the sun bathe her face. The air smelled of pine trees and songs of birds. As she sat there listening to the whispers of nature and the voices of the mountains, she felt at peace.

The stories above demonstrate how nature affected the athletic life of Isabella Wakeham, a highly competitive and elite athlete. As mentioned in the previous chapter, Same but Different, the flip between competition and nature activities shines a light on the power nature has not only to change general mental health but also athletic mindsets. Isabella is probably one of the most successful athletes of my age. Because of that, the level of competition at which she consistently performs has inspired a curiosity within me.

Not only does she consistently dominate both her male and female competitors at local ninja competitions, but she is also an extremely successful athlete at the junior international and senior national levels. From watching her compete to listening to her amazing stories, I have become interested in the mental side of her athletic training and how she prepares herself mentally for training and competition. While her experiences in nature routinely allow her to exercise with increased ease and enjoyment that is not the *only* way she strengthens her mind.

According to Tim Ferris, while researching for his book *The Tools of Titans*, over **80 percent** of the 200 people he interviewed—successful people from a diversity of fields and industries, including athletes—engaged in some form of meditation. And while praying and meditation have their unique differences, Isabella primarily prepares herself for training, competition, and her general life through prayer. Both prayer and meditation seek to find a balance between the internal and external forces that impact life. Whether meditating in nature with Ronna Schneberger or praying like my friend did in the ready room of the biggest competition of her life, the power of taking time to break away from the noise and stress of this world can have amazing effects on the mind.

According to a *Mindworks* blog post on why meditation is important, meditation has been shown to make people happier. Through countless research studies of people meditating, mood-enhancing and happiness-boosting proved to be a common theme. Next, just like spending time in nature, meditation helps the individual manage anxiety, stress, and depression. Through different techniques and mindfulness exercises, just like with the chemicals produced by trees, stress, anxiety, and depression are reduced. And in a study by the University of Wisconsin, researchers could see that meditation truly had psychological effects on the brain. When practiced regularly, the part of the brain that regulates stress and anxiety shrinks.

Another huge benefit of meditation is that anyone can do it, regardless of age, experience, or background. As with nature, the all-encompassing aspect of meditation allows it to be extremely accessible to everybody, including those who need it most but might not have the financial privileges to support themselves. Finally, meditation has remarkably quick results. Maybe the amazing results do not appear immediate to all, but with dedication and continual practice, their effects begin to become present and obvious.

From the positive results above, it is no wonder more than 80 percent of the successful people Tim Ferris interviewed credited meditation as one of their habits of success. And while the specific type of meditation I am emphasizing is nature meditation (spending thoughtful, quiet time in nature), clearly, *any* form of meditation or mindful recovery helps improve mental well-being.

When Tim Ferris first realized that meditation could have drastic positive effects on the mind, he, like many others, was initially hesitant about the idea. He was afraid that it would take away from being driven, aggressive, and productive, but as soon as he started practicing, he found it was quite the opposite.

"Meditation simply helps you channel your drive toward the few things that matter, rather than every moving target and imaginary opponent that pops up."

—TIM FERRIS

The world of athletics requires constant training, and concepts like nature meditation can seem completely absurd. Consider those who have come before us and the behaviors that made them successful, both physically and mentally. Maybe the idea of setting aside time to do nothing but be in nature will begin to make a little more sense.

RECAP

KEY TAKEAWAYS:

- Appreciating both the **small** and **big** aspects of the athletic **journey** is essential.
- **Meditation** is one of the most productive things one can do for their athletic career.

CHAPTER 15

ATHLETES BY NATURE

TAKING TIME TO BE IN NATURE

Through the previous two chapters, we have looked once more into the minds of athletes uncovering part of what makes them elite competitors. We looked not at their mental game during training and competition but at how their athletic life interacted with and was affected by the presence of nature.

I am most drawn to the ocean. As an athlete, whether it is training in open water or simply resting in the waves and poetry of the sea, being in that aspect of nature not only brings me peace but inspires me in the competition pool as well.

For Isabella, an incredible athlete and American Ninja Warrior, nature and meditation gave her a natural flow when exercising. They helped her reach mental calm before challenging and high-pressure competitions, respectively.

And the truly interesting thing is that when both I and my ninja friend were in nature, we experienced the full gifts of nature's powers. Even though neither of us sought nature solely to gain an edge, restore peace and mental rest, or mentally to get into the zone and find flow, we achieved just that. All the incredible effects that nature has on the mind that I explored throughout What I Call Nature Magic seamlessly translated into my athletic mind as well.

"In high school, the kids who out-trained everybody were the ones who won. But in the more elite levels of sport, it's those who out-rest everyone else who become the greatest."

—MICHAEL MARSH, THREE-TIME OLYMPIC MEDALIST

I talked about this a little in the previous chapter, but I would like to touch again on the topic of hustle-culture. The way my dad defined hustle-culture, and the way I now define it, is the societal idea that busy work equals productivity. It is the idea that to be great, you have to work hard all the time, and that recovery actually wastes the time that could be spent working. It is the idea that prioritizing sleep means you will end up being *behind* (physically or intellectually) those who use the night hours to train, study, work, or just *do* more. It is a warped concept that puts the view of 'more is more' *over* the long-held and usually accurate view of less is more. In this hustle-culture society, the idea of dedicating time to be in nature can seem counterproductive and possibly even a waste of time. Yet if it works for me and my friend and for various elite athletes and successful individuals (according to Tim Ferris), maybe it is not a waste of time after all.

Amanda Presgraves, who I interviewed previously, is one elite athlete who schedules her life around being in nature and similarly challenges the hustle-culture of our society by prioritizing spending time outdoors. Remember, Amanda is now a world-level competitive triathlete and swam competitively throughout her four years of college at a competitive Division 1 university. But while Amanda's athletic experience in college was, for the most part, a success, a double hip injury put her in recovery (and out of the sport) for several months. Amanda was interested in exploring passions and interests outside of swimming and studied abroad in the Philippines while recovering. She explored the natural side of the country as well by getting SCUBA certified, visiting rain forests, and climbing mountains.

Amanda's college experience as a student-athlete had its fair share of unfortunate mental health experiences. She revealed during our interview that she was one of the *only* members of her women's team who did not suffer from some sort of mental health issue while in college, and she accredited her strong mental health to her study abroad trip to the Philippines. The community support from that trip, the opportunity to visit amazing natural places, and the time to explore interests outside of her sport contributed to Amanda's strong mental health throughout and past college.

Since college, Amanda made an intentional decision to prioritize spending time in nature. Knowing that she truly loves spending time outdoors, I questioned her about her relationship with nature during our interview. In response, Amanda gave a rather long, but priceless, answer:

Definitely more so in the past few years, a lot of the movements that I enjoy take place outside: biking, mountain biking, trail running, swimming in lakes. And through all of that, [nature] fills a whole other side of my soul. Being in the fresh air, in the sunshine, I just feel like it hits the reset button. It's where I feel most like myself, and I feel presence and mindfulness. And, you know, I don't think I really had the opportunity truly to indulge in that before. I was just swimming all the time, and that's all there really was.

And it's one of the things I've been thinking about lately: I love [exercising in nature] so much because it's the one time where my thoughts are moving at the same pace in my body, and they connect and everything just like makes sense. And I truly look forward to those moments when I can get out and there's that connection. And I'm breathing the fresh air, and that reset button just takes place and I'm centered again. Yeah...I find my thoughts, I find myself, and it's just like this beautiful place of peace for me.

And then being able to enjoy it with other people on top of that is what has changed it. And because of my relationships and the access to outdoor recreation that kept me here [in Harrisonburg]. It's so accessible for me to just go fifteen minutes out into the woods. And I just have a really powerful and empowering group of women in this community—even the guys are always down for an adventure—who are always bettering themselves or bettering me. They show me what I'm capable of, and this absolutely inspired me to get outside.

And always knowing that I have someone to enjoy the outdoors with has also helped me because the outdoors can be a really scary place for people, really unfamiliar. You can feel very lonely. And you feel so small, and not everyone feels welcome into the outdoors. And for me, I didn't understand the place. I didn't know how to read a map, but only when I had that invitation and introduction from my community did I feel it was a safe haven. And I'm really grateful for that because my experiences outside would not be what they are if it weren't for my community and for all the people who have shown me the ropes and shown me how to protect nature and enjoy it too. And now it truly feels like I go home when I go outside. And in the past couple of years, nature's been something absolutely essential for my well-being.

Amanda Presgraves sums up perfectly how nature, athletics, and community all interact with each other to form a beautiful overlap that creates fitness, togetherness, and peace above it all. As Amanda emphasized, nature does not look the same to everyone. For some, the idea of the natural world is daunting and full of fear, and to others, me included, nature looks like an adventure waiting to happen. But as Amanda also showed, community has the power not only to unite people to *people* within nature but also people to *nature*. Because of Amanda's love for nature and the natural environment she is part of daily, her athletic life revolves around nature as well. But although this works for Amanda, not all elite athletes would be willing to change their sport to accommodate nature. Although it is convenient to train in natural environments, for many, the simple act of dedicating habitual time to be in nature as a physical and mental recovery is enough to restore peace, build community, and strengthen the mind.

ATHLETES BY NATURE

Just like Amanda, Michael Marsh, a three-time Olympic track and field medalist, is about to make his second appearance within this book. But unlike Amanda, during our interview, Michael brought up the topic of nature, how it affected his mind as an athlete, and how it interacted with his sport.

Before Michael began training with the track and field coach at the University of Houston, he trained and competed for UCLA. The UCLA campus was near the coast and only around fifteen minutes down the street from Santa Monica beach— one of the most beautiful beaches in the country and a beach with which Michael was very familiar. Growing up in Los Angeles, the ocean was always right around the corner. It was a constant aspect of nature that was close by and accessible, and by going to school in Los Angeles as well, that fact did not change. But throughout Michael's collegiate experience, his relationship with nature had a particularly interesting appeal.

As we talked, Michael painted a picture of how his training and recovery looked, emphasizing the increased need for recovery as his workouts became increasingly difficult. Eventually, sufficient recovery *every* day became critical for the physical health of the athletes. Michael's team started taking ice baths to help loosen their muscles and recoup from their extremely taxing workout regimen. But while most of the team engaged in ice baths in the training room, Michael and one of his best friends from high school, who also went to UCLA, would hop in the car and go to the beach instead. But they did not drive off to skip out on the recovery part of practice or to spend their time partying on the beach. They were intentional about spending time in nature for how it positively affected them.

As Michael explained to me, while Los Angeles weather is very nice, the coastal waters can still be chilly. So in theory, bathing in the waters of Santa Monica Beach was quite like the ice baths that the rest of the team were doing:

> *Even though California has good weather, if you ever touched the water, it's extremely cold. So especially this serves our purpose in the evenings. We wouldn't make it [to the beach] till about six or seven in the evening, when it was extremely cold, just like an ice bath. If you're going to go through the pain of getting into a lot of that cold, I figured you might as well have a good sunset around.*
>
> *And also the natural salts that are in the ocean, people try to duplicate that. In my day, we'd soak with some Epsom salt, but you have natural things in the ocean, and something about it was better than the ice bath. And I was pretty sure, I mean, science had proved this*

later, but we were both convinced that we were doing
something better than the ice bath.

And they were. From simply being in an aspect of nature as beautiful as California beaches, to soaking in the natural goodness of the environment, to having the icing on top of beautiful seaside sunsets to accompany them in their recovery, it is hard to believe there could be any *better* way to recover from an intense workout.

While the beach helped him with his sports-related recovery, Michael also had the blessing of experiencing the powers nature had on his mind as well. For him, spending time in nature gave him time to think, helped him clarify his athletic strategy, and gave him room to sort through any other problems that he had to work through. He also talked about how he would occasionally warm up or cool down on the beach itself, running barefoot along the coast and developing a sense of place and a heightened awareness of his own mind.

"I find that being away from people in solitude and in nature, I'm able to think through things in a much clearer way," Michael said as he recalled his experiences from being at the beach. "The beach was a great place to kind of think, and actually, I made some of the most important decisions that I had to make on the beach."

Unbeknownst to him, his habits around sports and the ocean are *exactly* the kind of habits that I seek to highlight and encourage within this book. The numerous benefits that I referred to in What I Call Nature Magic showed themselves clearly in Michael's sports life. The power of spending time in nature continues to impress me by how broad it is and the diversity of people it has the power to affect. This idea of nature being used to help mental and physical recovery is so important because, as seen through Michael's own athletic journey, it can have truly amazing effects.

While Michael and Amanda are both excellent examples of how nature can have positive effects on the athletic practices of athletes, they are not the *only* elite athletes who dedicate time to the outdoors. I have heard this pattern of nature as a place of recovery and peace for athletes in almost every athletic interview I had— whether from Victoria Garrick, who took a two-month break from her sport to prioritize her mental health; Jack Armstrong, who highlighted the importance of spending time outside as a way to reach a mental calm; or Elizabeth Beisel, whose love for the ocean shows itself in some of her environmental conservation advocacy work, the importance of nature is a critical and common theme.

Like our hustle-culture that makes it hard to slow down, our technology-driven and urbanized lives make it hard to find space for nature, especially in the downtown section of cities where the presence of nature can be hard to find. If you truly look, you realize it is not impossible. Whether it is in city parks or sidewalk greenery or maybe even a short trip away from the concrete jungle, we can find nature everywhere. In no way am I saying that you have to travel to paradise and back to experience the wonders of nature. However, it is still important to prioritize spending time in *some* form of nature regularly.

I know, even if nature is *there* and even if it can be found, it is increasingly difficult to make a habit of spending time in nature when it is not standing right in front of you. That is where community comes in. Just like Michael Marsh and his friend, or Amanda Presgraves and her Harrisonburg community, the help of others is almost essential. Whether it is an accountability partner or a fellow athlete who is also interested in spending more time in nature, community support has proved a common theme throughout the lives of these athletes who prioritize being in nature.

Spending time in the natural world can have remarkable effects on athletic minds and journeys. For as Anthony Douglas Williams said:

"Moments of solitude with Mother Nature are sunshine to the soul."

RECAP

KEY TAKEAWAYS:
- Spending time in nature can help you **physically** and **mentally recover** from your sport.
- Building a **community** around nature can help compound the positive effects of nature.

PART 4 - RETURNING TO THE MINDS OF ATHLETES SUMMARY:
Within Returning to the Minds of Athletes, I viewed four separate athletes, including myself, to better understand how nature has the power to affect athletes' minds. And whether it was through my story with the four different types of

swimming that highlighted how nature can affect athletes' minds, Isabella's story that highlighted the importance of meditation for the athletic journey, or the stories of Michael Marsh and Amanda Presgraves that showed how powerful community was in building a habit of spending time in nature, these athletes provided both valuable insight and a clearer view into how nature can be used to help support the mental health of elite athletes.

CHAPTER 16

OVERLAPPING WORLDS

———

*"People must feel that the natural world is
important and valuable and beautiful and
wonderful and an amazement and a pleasure."*

—DAVID ATTENBOROUGH

IT'S WHAT THE PROS DO

Mother Nature is an invaluable gift to our world. Its beauty
and diversity and support and power are enough to sustain almost any need we might ever have. Its presence is all
around us: in the sky and trees or in the mountains and in
wildlife. All we have to do is look for it and it will begin to
appear everywhere in life.

In the previous chapters, we discussed how the beauty of
nature has the power to positively affect the mind in wondrous ways. We discussed how meditation has incredible
power to help support the mind as well, just like spending
time in nature. In The Beauty of the Climb, I mentioned

the data found by Tim Ferris that highlighted how many successful people prioritize time to sit, think, and meditate. Tim Ferris, a well-regarded author, entrepreneur, and public speaker, has written several books (five in total), the most notable being *The 4-Hour Work Week*. While *all* his books are extremely educational, his fourth book, *The Tools of Titans*, highlighted a concept I found extremely interesting, a concept that inspired some of my research within this book: meditation has the power to give people a mental edge in their life, just like nature.

But before we can continue with our emphasis on nature and meditation for mental health, we must retouch upon the need to accept the diversity of mental health in the first place. I know, it's been a long time since we have talked about mental health issue stigmas in the sports world and the need for open conversation. Still, because this topic is so important, I believe that I should finish wrapping up our mental illness exploration before I wrap up this book.

Without general acceptance that our athletic minds need training and recovery just as much as our bodies, meditation and intentional time in nature will not be prioritized. My goal is not to *make* you believe what I believe but to show you *why* I believe what I believe and let you make your own choice. I encourage you to consider that even if you might not be struggling mentally, the readiness of your mind is a crucial component to being an elite athlete.

"Mindset was something that I excelled at naturally. That's what made me a good athlete. And it wasn't necessarily that I was stronger, bigger, taller. It wasn't the physical things but the mental things that really made the difference."

—REBECCA SONI

Several months ago, I had the pleasure of interviewing six-time Olympic medalist Rebecca Soni about nature, mental health, and her time as an athlete. While we covered significant ground on nature and being an Olympian, the intersection between sports and mental health was a critical point of insight within our conversation.

After retiring from the sport and realizing the identity loss that comes after leaving one's elite sport, Rebecca and fellow Olympian Caroline Burckle founded a powerful and impactful organization that highlights the importance of strong mental health for developing and retiring athletes. And as of now, RISE has thirty elite athlete mentors whose role is to support youth athletes on their mental and physical journey throughout the sport.[4]

"[RISE's] journey is about making a difference," it reads from RISE Athletes' website as of July 2, 2021 (a quote

---

4   This is not an advertisement for RISE Athletes, nor am I recommending that you participate in the program. The RISE Athletes program might be expensive, but its mission to help young athletes with their mental health is still extremely important.

that had disappeared from the website by October 1, 2021). "It is about connecting the physical body with the brain and teaching the fundamentals of mental health to teen athletes so they can take the tools with them on their journeys through sport and beyond."

"And you know the physical improves as we nurture the emotional and mental tools," Rebecca continues during our interview as she describes RISE Athletes. "And that also really does lead to better self-awareness, better mental health."

Rebecca is one of many athletes who has made it her mission to speak up, raise awareness, and inspire change within the athletic community around the topics of mental health. The stigma still has not fallen yet, but the cracks are appearing. The more each of us takes a stand and chooses to be open with our teammates and fellow athletes about mental health struggles within our sports, the more cracks will begin to appear, until one day, the stigma will fall.

Nature meditation and advocacy around mental health in athletic communities go hand in hand. Both are needed to help shift the athletic culture from prioritizing victories over the health of the athletes themselves to a culture where athletes can thrive both physically *and* mentally. And while the advocacy toward breaking the mental health stigmas in athletic communities will create an openness for vulnerability and conversation, Nature's place in this equation is helping strengthen, maintain, and reinforce strong mental health in the athletes so that they can succeed both in and out of their sport.

I often find it challenging to be radically different, to openly challenge the mental health stigmas or to prioritize nature meditation as part of my athletic training. Usually, all I need is a little inspiration so I know that I am not alone in what I am doing and have confidence that I am headed in the right direction. For those of you who feel the same, use all the names within this book as *your* inspiration to be different and help make a change both in your own athletic life and in the athletic community as a whole. Explore nature with curiosity and challenge those stigmas with passion because, if for no other reason, it's what the pros do.

BALANCING THE OVERLAP

For this entire book, we have looked at mental health, sports, and nature in different chapters and sections, but until this chapter, we really haven't looked at them as one whole topic. After starting out by looking at the relationship between sports and mental health, we then transitioned into our exploration of how nature and mental health interacted. Now, as we wrap up this journey, it is time to bring these three topics together.

I started this book to explore how nature plays a role in strengthening, reinforcing, and maintaining the mental health of elite athletes. I can confidently say that I have done so in full. Through months of researching, studying, interviewing, and recounting personal experiences, it is clear to me that nature truly does have the potential to help strengthen, maintain, and reinforce the mental health of elite athletes.

Whether you are unaware that they are struggling, suspect that you might be struggling but don't want to get a diagnosis, or are afraid to self-diagnose, nature will help regardless. Whether you go to the beach, go to the mountains, go to the park, or simply buy a potted plant for your downtown apartment, nature will work her wonders.

> "When was the last time you spent a quiet moment just doing nothing –just sitting and looking at the sea, or watching the wind blowing the tree limbs, or waves rippling on a pond, a flickering candle or children playing in the park?"
>
> —RALPH MARSTON

Being an athlete, whether elite or not, is not easy. The amount of physical stress we voluntarily put on our bodies is extreme, but the amount of stress we put on our minds can be even more. Improving mental health is a journey, not a one-time accomplishment, but as we begin to train and recover our bodies *and* minds, the outcomes will be outstanding. The overlap between sports, mental health, and nature is unique, to say the least. Nonetheless, it has the potential for incredible change.

A couple of months ago, Simone Manuel posted a gratitude post after making the Olympic team in the 50m free. Simone thanked her supporters, highlighting the difficult parts and giving praise for the wonderful memories. She ended her post with a quote that I have not let go:

"Success is not in the victory. It is in the fight you bring."

—SIMONE MANUEL

This is to you, dear athletes, whether you win the race or game or competition, or you don't. Do your best until you cross the finish line. If you truly do your best by training hard, recovering well, and supporting those around you, then you have already succeeded.

That is the true beauty of those three overlapping worlds.

ACKNOWLEDGMENTS

———

I would like to take some time to acknowledge those who have given this book, and the stories within it wings strong enough to fly. Thank you for being such a wonderful part of my life and helping me spread this message to the world.

First, I would like to give a *HUGE* thank you to my publishing company, New Degree Press, along with Eric Koester, Michael Butler, Sandy Huffman, and all the other editors who helped me refine my voice into something greater than I could have ever imagined.

I'd also like gratefully to acknowledge my Village of supporters who helped me fund this book, turning it from just a dream into a reality:

Milena Nino, Elisabeth Walla, Ann Barnes, Amanda Presgraves, Lucy and Sam Oke, Ellie Bartlett, Craig Cordola, Allison Cordola, Maarten Dullaert, Lisa Linerode, Don Taylor, Manuel FragoSo Abbey Murff, Lily Yee, Jenny Murff, Cate Gilbert, Komal Shah, Shannon Stewart, Eric Koester, Leigh McLeroy, Chasity Jennings-Nunez, Chinyere Eigege, Melvin

Maresh, Justin Ryan Bennett, Michelle Jones, Marva L. Lawrence, The Anands, Joseph Casas, Kaylin Slaughter, Terry Parker, Ziz Abdur-Raoof, Joseph Angelle, Vera Armstrong, Preethi Chinta, Tyndall Wakeham, Vanessa Krantzcke, Elizabeth Erin Stanley, Angela Stangl, Michael Andrew Lewis, Gambrill Wagner, Helen Wagner, Franzeta Zanielle Boleware-Bradley, Beier/Stickney Family, Angela Malone, LayKian Spillman, Michael Barnes Jr., Meggan Watson, Imani Parker, Gizelle Shadid, Jennifer Hong, Fabienne Vailes, Prisca Franklin, Benjamin Liff, Jackie Braden, Jonathan Mueller, Tim and Rebecca Barnes, Kamilla Rivera-Leyden, Laura Ellen Huebner-Diaz, Karen D. Marshall, Suzette Gum, Barbara Ross, Danny Jennings, Jennifer Jordan, Livia Woolery, Tara Soma, Chris Woolery, Merin Noonan, Sylvia Choy, Michael Barnes, Marna Marsh, Julia Aldrich, Danielle Miller, Michael L. Marsh, Peter Hostrawser, Carlos Solis, Cindy Byrd, and Brian Angelle.

Lastly, I'd like to acknowledge a few sources of inspiration. These are the people who encouraged me to think, explore, and be different, and the people who motivated me to try to change the world:

Matthew Barnes, Ann Barnes, Elizabeth Barnes, Benjamin Barnes, Michael Phelps, Elizabeth Beisel, Victoria Garrick, Brené Brown, Ronna Schneberger, Nooshin Razani, Rebecca Soni, Michael Marsh, Jack Armstrong, Amanda Presgraves, Miranda Noonan, Ziz Abdur-Raoof, Shannon Stewart, Isabella Wakeham, and Dirk Marshall.

And thank you, God, for everything else.

APPENDIX

INTRODUCTION

Florio, John, and Ouisie Shapiro. "The Dark Side of Going for Gold." *The Atlantic,* August 18, 2016. https://www.theatlantic. com/health/archive/2016/08/post-olympic-depression/496244/.

Miller, Anna Medaris. "Olympic Athletes Say They Face 'an Epidemic' of Suicide and Depression in Michael Phelps' HBO documentary." *Insider,* July 29, 2020. https://www.insider.com/ michael-phelps-weight-of-gold-olympians-suicide-depression-epidemic-2020-7.

CHAPTER 1 — BEHIND THE MINDS OF ATHLETES

NBC Sports. "Michael Phelps, Jason Lezak, and the Greatest Relay in Olympic History | NBC Sports." March 28, 2020. Video, 5:08. https://youtu.be/zpuzRseheFg.

USA Swimming. "All-Time Top Relay Splits." Accessed September 20, 2021. https://www.usaswimming.org/times/data-hub/all-time-relay-splits.

USA Swimming. "World/US Record Progressions." Accessed September 20, 2021. https://www.usaswimming.org/times/data-hub/record-progressions.

CHAPTER 2 – MICHAEL MARSH

PeterMacca88. "World Championships in Athletics 1993–200 Metres Men." October 23, 2013. Video, 4:51. https://youtu.be/Cd4F_O5NuZo.

CHAPTER 3 – JACK ARMSTRONG

Armstrong, Keith. "FINA Junior Worlds in Budapest 4x100 Free Relay Prelims." August 20, 2019. Video, 4:53. https://youtu.be/s4XcePSuTlo.

CHAPTER 4 – ELIZABETH BEISEL

Beisel, Elizabeth. *Silver Lining.* Mukwonago: Nico 11 Publishing & Design, 2020.

CHAPTER 5 – DEFINING MENTAL HEALTH

American Psychiatric Association. "What Is Mental Illness?" Accessed September 21, 2021. https://www.psychiatry.org/patients-families/what-is-mental-illness.

Barnes, Matthew, and Fabienne Vailes. "Episode 33: Fabienne Vailes, Co-Author of '*How to Grow a Grown Up.*'" April 14, 2021. In *The Education Game with Matt Barnes and Dr. Scott Van Beck.* Produced by Matthew Barnes. Podcast, 54:53. https://open.spotify.com/episode/2ZIGFJR3AikCAamMy1CSPX.

TEDx Talks. "Athletes and Mental Health: The Hidden Opponent | Victoria Garrick | TEDxUSC." June 2, 2017. Video, 21:13. https://youtu.be/Sdk7pLpbIls.

CHAPTER 6 – SHAME AND STIGMAS

Brown, Brené. *Daring Greatly.* New York City: Avery Publishing, 2012.

Brown, Brené. "Listening To Shame." Filmed March 2012 in Long Beach, CA. TED video, 20:22. https://www.ted.com/talks/brene_brown_listening_to_shame/transcript.

Merriam-Webster. s.v. "shame (*n.*)." Accessed September 22, 2021. https://www.merriam-webster.com/dictionary/shame.

Merriam-Webster. s.v. "stigma (*n.*)." Accessed September 22, 2021. https://www.merriam-webster.com/dictionary/stigma.

National Alliance on Mental Illness. "Mental Health by the Numbers." Last modified March 2021. https://nami.org/mhstats.

Rössler, Wulf. "The Stigma of Mental Disorders." *EMBO Reports* 17, No. 9 (2016): 1250-53. https://www.embopress.org/doi/epdf/10.15252/embr.201643041.

CHAPTER 7 – THE WEIGHT OF GOLD

Athletes for Hope. "Mental Health and Athletes." Accessed September 20, 2021. http://www.athletesforhope.org/2019/05/mental-health-and-athletes/.

Florio, John, and Ouisie Shapiro. "The Dark Side of Going for Gold." *The Atlantic,* August 18, 2016. https://www.theatlantic.com/health/archive/2016/08/post-olympic-depression/496244/.

HBO. "The Weight of Gold (2020): Official Trailer | HBO." July 20, 2020. Video, 2:25. https://youtu.be/LzGdIh3ciSk.

Miller, Anna Medaris. "Olympic Athletes Say They Face 'an Epidemic' of Suicide and Depression in Michael Phelps' HBO documentary." *Insider,* July 29, 2020. https://www.insider.com/michael-phelps-weight-of-gold-olympians-suicide-depression-epidemic-2020-7.

TED. "The Danger of A Single Story | Chimamanda Ngozi Adichie." October 7, 2009. Video, 19:16. https://youtu.be/D9Ihs241zeg.

CHAPTER 8 – IF YOU WANT TO GO FAR

Gilbert, Stephanie. "The Importance of Community and Mental Health." National Alliance on Mental Illness, November 18, 2019. Accessed September 20, 2021. https://nami.org/Blogs/NAMI-Blog/November-2019/The-Importance-of-Community-and-Mental-Health.

CHAPTER 9 – SPEAKING FOR THOSE UNHEARD

Fieldstadt, Elisha, and Conor Murray. "Simone Biles Is the Latest Athlete Vocal about Mental Health." NBC News, July 28, 2021. https://www.nbcnews.com/news/olympics/simone-biles-latest-athlete-vocal-about-mental-health-n1275218.

McDowell, Erin. "12 Athletes Who've Spoken about Their Mental Health Struggles." Insider, June 6, 2021. https://www.insider.com/athletes-mental-health-struggles-depression-2021-6.

TEDx Talks. "Athletes and Mental Health: The Hidden Opponent | Victoria Garrick | TEDxUSC." June 2, 2017. Video, 21:13. https://youtu.be/Sdk7pLpbIls.

Victoria Garrick. "Victoria Garrick 2020 Speaking Tour | Student-Athlete Mental Health Advocate." October 1, 2020. Video, 6:13. https://youtu.be/MdGihyiyZLM.

CHAPTER 10 – NATURE AND NURTURE

Barnes, Marni, and Clare Cooper Marcus. Gardens in Healthcare Facilities: Uses, Therapeutic Benefits, and Design Recommendation. Martinez, CA: The Center for Health Design, Inc., 1995.

Parris, Aer. "Hospitals Find Gardens Help with Healing." REI Co-Op, August 29, 2019. Accessed September 20, 2021. https://www.rei.com/blog/stewardship/hospitals-find-gardens-help-with-healing.

TEDx Talk. "Prescribing Nature for Health | Nooshin Razani | TEDxNashville." June 14, 2016. Video, 17:47. https://youtu. be/oukoQriYYws.

World Wildlife Fund, Inc. "Why It's Important That We Value Nature." Accessed September 19, 2021. https://www.wwf.org. uk/what-we-do/valuing-nature.

CHAPTER 11 – FOLLOW YOUR HEART... BUT TAKE YOUR BRAIN WITH YOU

Fitzgerald, Sunny. "The Secret to Mindful Travel? A Walk in the Woods." *National Geographic*, October 18, 2019. https://www. nationalgeographic.com/travel/article/forest-bathing-nature-walk-health.

Li, Q., K. Morimoto, A. Nakadai, H. Inagaki, M. Katsumata, T. Shimizu, Y. Hirata, et al. "Forest Bathing Enhances Human Natural Killer Activity and Expression of Anti-Cancer Proteins." *International Journal of Immunopathology and Pharmacology* 20, no. 2 (April 2007), 3–8. https://doi. org/10.1177/03946320070200S202.

Li, Q., K. Morimoto, M. Kobayashi, H. Inagaki, M. Katsumata, Y. Hirata, K. Hirata, et al. "Visiting a Forest, but Not a City, Increases Human Natural Killer Activity and Expression of Anti-Cancer Proteins." *International Journal of Immunopathology and Pharmacology* 21, no. 1 (January 2008), 117–27. https:// doi.org/10.1177/039463200802100113.

Niiler, Eric. "'Blue Mind' Explores the Calming Effect That Water Has on People." *The Washington Post,* July 28, 2014. https:// www.washingtonpost.com/national/health-science/blue-mind-explores-the-calming-effect-that-water-has-on-people/2014/07/28/471d7a5a-11bb-11e4-9285-4243a40ddc97_story.html.

Richardson, Miles, Adam Cormack, Lucy McRobert, Ralph Under-hill. "30 Days Wild: Development and Evaluation of a Large-

Scale Nature Engagement Campaign to Improve Well-Being."
PLoS One 11, no. 2 (February 2016): e0149777. https://doi.
org/10.1371/journal.pone.0149777.

Southwark Carers. "Getting Out into Nature." Accessed September 21, 2021. https://www.southwarkcarers.org.uk/enriching/
health-and-wellbeing/staying-healthy/getting-out-into-nature/.

TEDx Talks. "Those Who Are "Nature-Wise" Have an Edge in
Today's World | Ronna Schneberger | TEDxCanmore." February 6, 2017. Video, 15:35. https://youtu.be/kYNpQuojIyE.

CHAPTER 12 – THE POWER OF NATURE

TEDx Talk. "Prescribing Nature for Health | Nooshin Razani |
TEDxNashville." June 14, 2016. Video, 17:47. https://youtu.
be/oukoQriYYws.

CHAPTER 14 – THE BEAUTY OF THE CLIMB

Brunette, Lisa. "Meditation Produces Positive Changes in the
Brain." *UW—Madison News,* February 6, 2003. https://news.
wisc.edu/meditation-produces-positive-changes-in-the-brain/.

Dube, Rob. "How Meditation Helped These Leaders Achieve
Extraordinary Success." Thrive Global, June 23, 2017. Accessed
September 20, 2021. https://medium.com/thrive-global/
how-meditation-helped-these-leaders-achieve-extraordinary-success-4c6c54ee1cc7.

Mindworks. "Why Is Meditation Important? 6 Facts You Need to
Know." Accessed September 19, 2021. https://mindworks.org/
blog/why-is-meditation-important-facts-you-need-to-know/.

National Ninja League. "Isabella Wakeham 1st Place Austin Ninjas
Cedar Park (#2) | National Ninja League Season 6." January 10,
2021. Video, 3:13. https://youtu.be/9tLBCy_xkdA.

CHAPTER 16 – OVERLAPPING WORLDS

Dube, Rob. "How Meditation Helped These Leaders Achieve Extraordinary Success." Thrive Global, June 23, 2017. Accessed September 20, 2021. https://medium.com/thrive-global/how-meditation-helped-these-leaders-achieve-extraordinary-success-4c6c54ee1cc7.

RISE Athletes. "What We Do." Home Page. Accessed October 1, 2021. https://www.rise-athletes.com/.

Simone Manuel. "Praise Him in Advance. To God Be the Glory!" *Instagram*, June 21, 2021. https://www.instagram.com/p/CQZ-TyfYgfWo/.